CONVERSATIONS IN SIMPLE ENGLISH

Short Natural Dialogues to
Boost Your Confidence &
Improve Your Spoken English

by Olly Richards

Edited by Connie Au-Yeung & Eleonora Calviello

*101 Conversations in Simple English: Short Natural Dialogues to Boost Your Confidence &
Improve Your Spoken English*

FREE STORYLEARNING® KIT

Discover how to learn foreign languages faster & more effectively through the power of story.

Your free video masterclasses, action guides & handy printouts include:

- A simple six-step process to maximise learning from reading in a foreign language

- How to double your memory for new vocabulary from stories

- Planning worksheet (printable) to learn faster by reading more consistently

- Listening skills masterclass: "How to effortlessly understand audio from stories"

- How to find willing native speakers to practise your language with

To claim your FREE StoryLearning® Kit, visit:

www.storylearning.com/kit

WE DESIGN OUR BOOKS TO BE INSTAGRAMMABLE!

Post a photo of your new book to Instagram

using #storylearning and you'll get an entry

into our monthly book giveaways!

Tag us **@storylearningpress** to make sure we see you!

BOOKS BY OLLY RICHARDS

Olly Richards writes books to help you learn languages through the power of story. Here is a list of all currently available titles:

Short Stories in Danish For Beginners

Short Stories in Dutch For Beginners

Short Stories in English For Beginners

Short Stories in French For Beginners

Short Stories in German For Beginners

Short Stories in Icelandic For Beginners

Short Stories in Italian For Beginners

Short Stories in Norwegian For Beginners

Short Stories in Brazilian Portuguese For Beginners

Short Stories in Russian For Beginners

Short Stories in Spanish For Beginners

Short Stories in Swedish For Beginners

Short Stories in Turkish For Beginners

Short Stories in Arabic for Intermediate Learners

Short Stories in English for Intermediate Learners

Short Stories in Italian for Intermediate Learners

Short Stories in Korean for Intermediate Learners
Short Stories in Spanish for Intermediate Learners

101 Conversations in Simple English
101 Conversations in Simple French
101 Conversations in Simple German
101 Conversations in Simple Italian
101 Conversations in Simple Spanish
101 Conversations in Simple Russian

101 Conversations in Intermediate English
101 Conversations in Intermediate French
101 Conversations in Intermediate German
101 Conversations in Intermediate Italian
101 Conversations in Intermediate Spanish

101 Conversations in Mexican Spanish
101 Conversations in Social Media Spanish
World War II in Simple Spanish

All titles are also available as audiobooks. Just search your favourite store!

For more information visit Olly's author page at:
www.storylearning.com/books

ABOUT THE AUTHOR

 Olly Richards is a foreign language expert and teacher. He speaks eight languages and has authored over 30 books. He has appeared in international press, from the BBC and the Independent to El País and Gulf News. He has featured in language documentaries and authored language courses for the Open University.

Olly started learning his first foreign language at the age of 19, when he bought a one-way ticket to Paris. With no exposure to languages growing up, and no natural talent for languages, Olly had to figure out how to learn French from scratch. Twenty years later, Olly has studied languages from around the world and is considered an expert in the field.

Through his books and website, StoryLearning.com, Olly is known for teaching languages through the power of story – including the book you are holding in your hands right now!

You can find out more about Olly, including a library of free training, at his website:

www.storylearning.com

CONTENTS

Introduction xv

How to Use this Book xvii

The Five-Step Reading Process xxiii

The Mystery of the Stolen Drawings.. 1

Character Profiles 3

Introduction to the Story... 5

1. Natalie and Alice 6

2. The journey to the market... 8

3. Camden Market 10

4. Robert Green's shop.. 12

5. Some very special drawings... 14

6. How did they get here?.. 16

7. The call... 18

8. A suspicious man 20

9. The news 22

10. The second robbery 24

11. Alice and Natalie in the café 26

12. The next step 28

13. At Lawrence Windsor's mansion 30

14. The reward 32

15. The key 34

16. The investigation 36

17. The interruption 38

18. Lawrence and Mariana 40

19. The second collection 42

20. The cleaner 44

21. The metal box.. 46

22. Charlie 48

23. The gardener 50

24. Artur 52

25. The first suspect... 54

26. The cooks 56

27. The discussion 58

28. The nanny 60

29. The security guard 62

30. Daniel 64

31. The video footage 66

32. The person in the video footage 68

33. Two hats 70

34. The conclusions 72

35. Natalie and Mariana Windsor return 74

36. The promise 76

37. Alice tells Natalie what she knows 78

38. Natalie tells Alice what she knows 80

39. There he is again! 82

40. Following the man in the hat 84

41. The alleyway 86

42. The bookshop 88

43. Face to face with the man in the hat 90

44. The Historians' Club 92

45. What the man in the hat was doing at the market 94

46. What the man in the hat did next 96

47. The suspects 98

48. The man in the hat disappears 100

49. Pauline at the market 102

50. Back in Robert Green's shop 104

51. The memory 106

52. Natalie and Alice have doubts about Robert Green 108

53. In the pub 110

54. The plan 112

55. Back in the Windsor's house 114

56. The test 116

57. Crying 118

58. Mariana's confession 120

59. The trade-off 122

60. Little Nemo 124

61. Mariana, regretful 126

62. Mariana's plea to Robert Green 128

63. Forgiveness 130

64. The police 132

65. The telephone call 134

66. The meeting in the square 136

67. The plan with Detective Smith 138

68. The interrogation.. 140

69. A new suspect 142

70. The search for Michael Wright 144

71. The last location 146

72. The trip to Newcastle 148

73. The Newcastle arts festival 150

74. The chase.. 152

75. Michael Wright 154

76. Michael's story 156

77. The non-existent call 158

78. The deceit... 160

79. The return trip... 162

80. The escape 164

81. The chase.. 166

82. The bicycles 168

83. The fall 170

84. The plan 172

85. The distraction 174

86. The argument... 176

87. The gun! 178

88. Pete 180

89. The briefcase 182

90. Robert Green wakes up 184

91. The departure of Robert Green.. 186

92. The return of the drawings.. 188

93. The donation... 190

94. The reward 192

95. The opening 194

96. The offer.. 196

97. The second offer 198

98. Lawrence Windsor's speech... 200

99. The map 202

100. A special invitation 204

101. The Windsors.. 206

INTRODUCTION

If you've ever tried speaking English with a stranger, chances are it wasn't easy! You might have felt tongue-tied when you tried to recall words or verb conjugations. You might have struggled to keep up with the conversation, with English words flying at you at 100mph. Indeed, many students report feeling so overwhelmed with the experience of speaking English in the real world that they struggle to maintain motivation. The problem lies with the way English is usually taught. Textbooks and language classes break English down into rules and other "nuggets" of information in order to make it easier to learn. But that can leave you with a bit of a shock when you come to actually speak English out in the real world: "People don't speak like they do in my textbooks!" That's why I wrote this book.

101 Conversations in Simple English prepares you to speak English in the real world. Unlike the contrived and unnatural dialogues in your textbook, the 101 authentic conversations in this book offer you simple but authentic spoken English that you can study away from the pressure of face-to-face conversation. The conversations in this book tell the story of six people in London. You'll experience the story by following the conversations the characters have with one another. Written entirely in spoken English, the conversations give you the authentic experience of reading real English in a format that is convenient and accessible for a beginner (A2 on the Common European Framework of Reference).

The extensive, story-based format of the book helps you get used to spoken English in a natural way, with the words and phrases you see gradually emerging in your own spoken English as you learn them naturally through your reading. The book is packed with engaging learning material including short dialogues that you can finish in one sitting, helpful English definitions of difficult words, scene-setting introductions to each chapter to help you follow along, and a story that will have you gripped until the end. These learning features allow you to learn and absorb new words and phrases, and then activate them so that, over time, you can remember and use them in your own spoken English. You'll never find another way to get so much practice with real, spoken English!

Suitable for beginners and intermediate learners alike, *101 Conversations in Simple English* is the perfect complement to any English course and will give you the ultimate head start for using English confidently in the real world! Whether you're new to English and looking for an entertaining challenge, or you have been learning for a while and want to take your speaking to the next level, this book is the biggest step forward you will take in your English this year.

If you're ready, let's get started!

HOW TO USE THIS BOOK

There are many possible ways to use a resource such as this, which is written entirely in English. In this section, I would like to offer my suggestions for using this book effectively, based on my experience with thousands of students and their struggles.

There are two main ways to work with content in a foreign language:

1. Intensively
2. Extensively

Intensive learning is when you examine the material in great detail, seeking to understand all the content - the meaning of vocabulary, the use of grammar, the pronunciation of difficult words, etc. You will typically spend much longer with each section and, therefore, cover less material overall. Traditional classroom learning, generally involves intensive learning. *Extensive* learning is the opposite of intensive. To learn extensively is to treat the material for what it is – not as the object of language study, but rather as content to be enjoyed and appreciated. To read a book for pleasure is an example of extensive reading. As such, the aim is not to stop and study the language that you find, but rather to read (and complete) the book.

There are pros and cons to both modes of study and, indeed, you may use a combination of both in your approach.

However, the "default mode" for most people is to study *intensively*. This is because there is the inevitable temptation to investigate anything you do not understand in the pursuit of progress and hope to eliminate all mistakes. Traditional language education trains us to do this. Similarly, it is not obvious to many readers how extensive study can be effective. The uncertainty and ambiguity can be uncomfortable: "There's so much I don't understand!"

In my experience, people have a tendency to drastically overestimate what they can learn from intensive study, and drastically underestimate what they can gain from extensive study. My observations are as follows:

- **Intensive learning**: Although it is intuitive to try to "learn" something you don't understand, such as a new word, there is no guarantee you will actually manage to "learn" it! Indeed, you will be familiar with the feeling of trying to learn a new word, only to forget it shortly afterwards! Studying intensively is also time-consuming meaning you can't cover as much material.

- **Extensive learning**: By contrast, when you study extensively, you cover huge amounts of material and give yourself exposure to much more content in the language than you otherwise would. In my view, this is the primary benefit of extensive learning. Given the immense size of the task of learning a foreign language, extensive learning is the only way to give yourself the exposure to the language that you need in order to stand a chance of acquiring it. You simply can't learn everything you need in the classroom!

When put like this, extensive learning may sound quite compelling! However, there is an obvious objection: "But how do I *learn* when I'm not looking up or memorising things?" This is an understandable doubt if you are used to a traditional approach to language study. However, the truth is that you can learn an extraordinary amount *passively* as you read and listen to the language, but only if you give yourself the opportunity to do so! Remember, you learned your mother tongue passively. There is no reason you shouldn't do the same with a second language!

Here are some of the characteristics of studying languages extensively:

Aim for completion When you read material in a foreign language, your first job is to make your way through from beginning to end. Read to the end of the chapter or listen to the entire audio without worrying about things you don't understand. Set your sights on the finish line and don't get distracted. This is a vital behaviour to foster because it trains you to enjoy the material before you start to get lost in the details. This is how you read or listen to things in your native language, so it's the perfect thing to aim for!

Read for gist The most effective way to make headway through a piece of content in another language is to ask yourself: "Can I follow the gist of what's going on?" You don't need to understand every word, just the main ideas. If you can, that's enough! You're set! You can understand and enjoy a great amount with gist alone, so carry on through the material and enjoy the feeling of making progress! If the material is so hard that you struggle to understand even the gist, then my advice for you would be to consider easier material.

Don't look up words As tempting as it is to look up new words, doing so robs you of time that you could spend reading the material. In the extreme, you can spend so long looking up words that you never finish what you're reading. If you come across a word you don't understand... Don't worry! Keep calm and carry on. Focus on the goal of reaching the end of the chapter. You'll probably see that difficult word again soon, and you might guess the meaning in the meantime!

Don't analyse grammar Similarly to new words, if you stop to study verb tenses or verb conjugations as you go, you'll never make any headway with the material. Try to *notice* the grammar that's being used (make a mental note) and carry on. Have you spotted some unfamiliar grammar? No problem. It can wait. Unfamiliar grammar rarely prevents you from understanding the gist of a passage but can completely derail your reading if you insist on looking up and studying every grammar point you encounter. After a while, you'll be surprised by how this "difficult" grammar starts to become "normal"!

You don't understand? Don't worry! The feeling you often have when you are engaged in extensive learning is: "I don't understand". You may find an entire paragraph that you don't understand or that you find confusing. So, what's the best response? Spend the next hour trying to decode that difficult paragraph? Or continue reading regardless? (Hint: It's the latter!) When you read in your mother tongue, you will often skip entire paragraphs you find boring, so there's no need to feel guilty about doing the same when reading English. Skipping difficult passages of text may feel like cheating, but it can, in fact, be a mature approach to reading that allows you to make progress through the material and, ultimately, learn more.

If you follow this mindset when you read English, you will be training yourself to be a strong, independent English learner who doesn't have to rely on a teacher or rule book to make progress and enjoy learning. As you will have noticed, this approach draws on the fact that your brain can learn many things naturally, without conscious study. This is something that we appear to have forgotten with the formalisation of the education system. But, speak to any accomplished language learner and they will confirm that their proficiency in languages comes not from their ability to memorise grammar rules, but from the time they spend reading, listening to, and speaking the language, enjoying the process, and integrating it into their lives.

So, I encourage you to embrace extensive learning, and trust in your natural abilities to learn languages, starting with... The contents of this book!

THE FIVE-STEP READING PROCESS

Here is my suggested five-step process for making the most of each conversation in this book:

1. Read the short introduction to the conversation. This is important, as it sets the context for the conversation, helping you understand what you are about to read. Take note of the characters who are speaking and the situation they are in. If you need to refresh your memory of the characters, refer to the character introductions at the front of the book.

2. Read the conversation all the way through without stopping. Your aim is simply to reach the end of the conversation, so do not stop to look up words and do not worry if there are things you do not understand. Simply try to follow the gist of the conversation.

3. Go back and read the same conversation a second time. If you like, you can read in more detail than before, but otherwise simply read it through one more time, using the vocabulary list to check unknown words and phrases where necessary.

4. By this point, you should be able to follow the gist of the conversation. You might like to continue to read the same conversation a few more times until you feel confident. This is time well-spent and with each repetition you will gradually build your understanding of the content.

5. Move on! There is no need to understand every word in the conversation, and the greatest value to be derived from the book comes from reading it through to completion! Move on to the next conversation and do your best to enjoy the story at your own pace, just as you would any other book.

At every stage of the process, there will inevitably be words and phrases you do not understand or passages you find confusing. Instead of worrying about the things you *don't* understand, try to focus instead on everything that you *do* understand, and congratulate yourself for the hard work you are putting into improving your English.

THE MYSTERY OF THE STOLEN DRAWINGS

Translated by Lucy Daghorn

CHARACTER PROFILES

Natalie

Natalie is a very observant and curious young woman. She studied History of Art at Oxford University in England. Her parents are English but she has lived in Spain all of her life. She loves to read, visit museums and draw.

Alice

Alice is a 28-year-old writer who writes mystery novels for an important English publishing company. She lives in Spain, with Natalie, but she loves to travel in England, her native country. Unlike Natalie, she does not like history and does not know much about art. She prefers reading mystery novels, watching horror movies and loves the outdoors.

Laurence Windsor

Laurence Windsor is a wealthy middle-aged man. He is the father of a young girl, named Mariana. Laurence has always been an avid art collector and his most prized collection contains a number of important 18th and 19th century English art works, including a number of paintings by the legendary English artist, William Turner.

Mariana Windsor

Mariana is the daughter of Laurence and she has inherited his love for collections. Mariana's greatest passion is her collection of rare comics, which she passes her days reading in her bedroom.

Robert Green

Robert Green is an antiques dealer who has a shop in one of London's oldest antiques markets. Robert is known for not being picky about the objects he receives. He will accept stolen objects and is just as ready to swindle the sellers he obtains objects from as he is to prey on innocent buyers. However, Robert doesn't know very much about art, so he would not be capable of recognising a truly valuable work, even if it was right under his nose....

The Man in the Hat

This mysterious character has been seen visiting London's antiques market and museums a lot lately. Nobody knows much about him, except that he seems to have a passion for art and history and he always keeps the brim of his hat down so it is hard to catch a clear glimpse of his face.

INTRODUCTION TO THE STORY

Natalie, a young art historian, travels to England with her friend, Alice.

One day, while wandering through an antiques market in London, the friends see a collection of beautiful paintings which immediately draw Natalie's attention. Before long, Natalie recognises one of the paintings as an original work by the legendary English painter, William Turner. But why would one of Turner's paintings be on sale in an old antiques market?

Natalie and Alice decide to speak with the owner of the market stall to find out. The stall owner, Robert Green, tells them that a few days ago, a strange man sold him the paintings. He explains however, that he did not realise they were original works and that he did not pay very much for them. Natalie begins to worry, realising that the artworks must be stolen....

Robert promises the girls that he will contact a friend who is an expert in English art and ask him to examine the paintings and verify their authenticity. He tells them that if the paintings turn out to be stolen, he will call the police the next day to report the crime. Natalie and Alice decide to take Robert at his word and leave the market, promising to return the next day to find out what happens. But as they leave, neither of them can shake the feeling that something is not right about the whole situation....

1. NATALIE AND ALICE

Natalie and Alice are on holiday in London. They have known each other for several years, since university. Natalie is an art historian and Alice is an author of crime and mystery books. They are in the hotel on the first day of their trip. It's a hot and sunny day.

Alice: Morning Natalie! How did you sleep?

Natalie: Great! You?

Alice: Yeah, me too. What do you want to do today?

Natalie: Hmm…. I feel like going to a market!

Alice: Great! A food market?

Natalie: No, I want to go to an antiques market.

Alice: Sounds good. Do you know of one?

Natalie: No, I'll have a look on my phone…. There's one in Camden Market.

Alice: Perfect. Does it open on Saturdays?

Natalie: Yes, it opens early morning every Saturday. It's 11 now.

Alice: Perfect! Where is it?

Natalie: Funnily enough, it's in an area called Camden, in North London…. It's a bit far. We can get a cab.

Alice: Sounds good. Let's go!

2. THE JOURNEY TO THE MARKET

Natalie and Alice leave the hotel and look for a cab to go to Camden Market.

Natalie: I don't see any cabs. Do you?

Alice: There's one! Put your hand out.

Natalie: Hello!

Cab driver: Hello! Where are you going?

Alice: We are going to Camden Market.

Cab driver: Camden Market. Ok, jump in. They've got everything there. What are you going to buy?

Natalie: Well, I'm an art historian, so I love antiques.

Cab driver: How interesting! London is a city full of art. Are you an art historian too?

Alice: No, I'm a writer.

Cab driver: Wow! What do you write?

Alice: I write crime and mystery books.

Cab driver: How interesting! There are also mysteries in Camden Market....

Alice: Really?

Cab driver: Of course! There are many stolen objects in Camden Market....

3. CAMDEN MARKET

Natalie and Alice arrive at Camden Market.

Alice: Wow! Look at all this stuff Natalie.

Natalie: It's amazing! There are so many shops, and loads of people.

Alice: Look at this watch! Is it an antique?

Natalie: Yes, it looks very old.

Alice: And that painting? Is it an original?

Natalie: It looks like an original.

Alice: Do you think it's expensive?

Natalie: I don't think so. Let's ask.... Good morning. How much does that painting cost?

Seller: Good morning. It costs 50 pounds. Are you interested?

Alice: No thanks. We were just wondering.

Natalie: And this watch, how much is it?

Seller: The watch costs 130 pounds. It's very old.

Natalie: Thanks!

Alice: Do you think it's stolen?

Natalie: I don't know. Maybe! There's no way of knowing.

Alice: Look at that small shop. It looks interesting. Do you want to go in?

Natalie: Of course, let's go.

4. ROBERT GREEN'S SHOP

Natalie and Alice enter a small antiques shop in Camden Market.

Robert Green: Good morning!

Natalie and Alice: Good morning!

Robert Green: My name is Robert Green. Welcome to my shop. Let me know if you have any questions.

Natalie: Nice to meet you. We are just going to have a look around.

Robert Green: Great!

Alice: Wow, so many beautiful items. There are so many works of art. Do you like them?

Natalie: Yes, it's really beautiful stuff; paintings, sculptures, drawings, books... even comics!

Alice: Do you think some of them could be stolen?

Natalie: Ha ha ha! I don't know. Why?

Alice: I like mysteries!

Natalie: There are no mysteries here, Alice, just art.... Wait! Look at this! I can't believe it!

5. SOME VERY SPECIAL DRAWINGS

In a shop in Camden Market, Natalie sees some drawings that catch her eye.

Natalie: I know these drawings! They are by Turner.

Alice: Who is Turner?

Natalie: William Turner was an English painter in the 18th century. One of the most important painters in British history!

Alice: Are you sure that these drawings are by him?

Natalie: Yes, I'm sure. I studied them at university.

Alice: Do you think they are originals?

Natalie: I'm almost certain. They look like originals…. But I can't believe it! What are they doing here? They only cost 100 pounds!

Alice: Should they be in a museum?

Natalie: Yes, they should be in a museum, a gallery or a collection.

Alice: What should we do?

Natalie: I don't know. Should we ask the shop owner?

Alice: Yes, that's a good idea.

6. HOW DID THEY GET HERE?

Natalie and Alice show Robert Green the drawings that they found in his shop and Natalie explains that she thinks they are originals by Turner.

Robert Green: You are telling me that these drawings are by Turner?!

Natalie: Yes, I'm almost certain. I'm an art historian. I know Turner's work. I know his paintings and his drawings. These are by Turner.

Robert Green: I can't believe it!

Alice: What are they doing here? How did they get here?

Robert Green: I don't know. Lots of people bring me works of art. I buy them and sell them to people who visit the shop.

Alice: Do you remember who brought these drawings?

Robert Green: Yes, I believe it was a man…. I don't remember what he looked like.

Alice: When did he bring you them?

Robert Green: This morning. Just a few hours ago.

Natalie: Do you think the drawings are stolen?

Robert Green: It's possible!

7. THE CALL

Robert Green tells Natalie and Alice that he has an idea for the Turner drawings.

Alice: What should we do?

Robert Green: I have an idea! I have a friend who is also an art historian. He's an expert in British art. His name is Michael Wood. He can tell you if the works really are by Turner. If they are, we will call the police.

Natalie: Okay, that sounds good.

Alice: That's a great idea.

Robert Green: I'll call him right now.... Hello? Hi, Michael. I need a favour. Can you come to the shop? I have some drawings that appear to be original works by Turner. Yes, William Turner! Okay, I'll see you then. Bye!

Alice: Is your friend coming now?

Robert Green: He says he's out of town. But he'll come by tomorrow. Do you want to come as well?

Natalie: Yes, that sounds good. I want to meet this expert and look at the works with him.

Robert Green: Well, see you tomorrow.

Natalie and Alice: See you tomorrow!

8. A SUSPICIOUS MAN

Natalie and Alice leave the shop to go back to the hotel. Before getting a cab, Alice tells Natalie that someone caught her attention in the shop.

Alice: There was a strange man in the shop.

Natalie: You mean Robert Green?

Alice: No. There was another man, a customer.

Natalie: What did he look like?

Alice: He was tall and he was wearing a hat…. There he is! He's the one leaving the shop now.

Natalie: Do you think there's something suspicious about him?

Alice: I don't know. There is definitely something strange about him….

Natalie: Do you think he's the thief?

Alice: I don't know, but I'm worried.

Natalie: Why are you worried?

Alice: Because that man in the hat knows that there are very valuable drawings in the shop.

9. THE NEWS

The next day, back at the hotel, Alice and Natalie are watching TV. The presenter announces breaking news.

TV Presenter: Works of art stolen in the centre of London! Valuable drawings by William Turner have disappeared from a private collection.

Natalie: I can't believe it! It's the three drawings from the shop!

Alice: It is! They are exactly the same; there's the drawing of a large church, the drawing of a boat on the shore and the drawing of a sleeping cat.

TV Presenter: So far there has been no trace of the thief, and the whereabouts of the drawings is unknown. The owner of the collection, Lawrence Windsor, is offering a large reward for the safe return of the works. A police investigation is under way.

Natalie: What should we do?

Alice: Should we call the police?

Natalie: No, let's go to Robert Green's shop. We'll call the police from there.

Alice: Okay, that makes sense. That way, no one will think he's a suspect.

10. THE SECOND ROBBERY

When Natalie and Alice arrive at the shop, they see that the police have already arrived. The shop windows are broken. Mr. Robert Green looks very upset.

Natalie: Hello, Mr. Green.

Robert Green: Here you are! Detective, these are the women from yesterday.

Alice: What's going on?

Robert Green: They are witnesses; the drawings were here yesterday. Someone stole them from the shop!

Natalie: Really?

Robert Green: She is an art historian. She can confirm that the drawings are by William Turner.

Natalie: Yes, I'm sure. They are the drawings from Lawrence Windsor's private collection! It's all over the news.

Detective Smith: Hello, I'm Detective Smith. Nice to meet you. Do you know who the thief is?

Natalie: No, I don't.

Alice: Maybe it's the man with the hat.

Detective Smith: The man with the hat?

Alice: Yes, a man in a hat was in the shop yesterday.

Detective Smith: Okay, well let's investigate him!

11. ALICE AND NATALIE IN THE CAFÉ

Natalie and Alice go to a café to talk about the stolen drawings.

Waiter: Good morning, what can I get you?

Natalie: Good morning. I would like a white coffee.

Alice: I'll have a breakfast muffin, please.

Waiter: Great! I will bring it all over.

Natalie: So, what do you think about the case?

Alice: Well…. There are two robberies. Yesterday someone stole the drawings from Lawrence Windsor's house. Today… or last night, someone stole them from Robert Green's shop.

Natalie: Do you think it's the same person?

Alice: Maybe! Perhaps the person who stole them from Lawrence Windsor's house didn't know how much they were worth. They are very valuable, but the person sold them for a small amount. So, after hearing about the robbery on TV, they found out the real price and went back to steal them again.

Natalie: There could also be a second thief.

Alice: That's true. Someone who overheard us in the shop....

Natalie: Someone like the mysterious man in the hat?

12. THE NEXT STEP

The waiter takes Natalie and Alice's order over to their table. The news about the robbery at Lawrence Windsor's mansion is on the TV.

Alice: Thank you. Could you bring us some sugar?

Waiter: Right away.

Alice: What should we do now?

Natalie: Well, nothing! Why do you want to do something? Detective Smith is working on the case.

Alice: But it's fun! I think we should go to Lawrence Windsor's house.

Waiter: Sorry for butting in, but Lawrence Windsor doesn't live in a house. He lives in a mansion!

Natalie: Is he rich?

Waiter: Yes, very rich. He has a huge art collection.

Alice: Do you know where he lives?

Waiter: Of course, it's just down the road near Hampstead Heath. You can see his mansion from here.

Alice: The bill, please!

13. AT LAWRENCE WINDSOR'S MANSION

After breakfast, Alice and Natalie cross the road in the direction of Lawrence Windsor's mansion to investigate the robbery of the drawings by Turner. They ring the bell and the owner comes to greet them.

Lawrence Windsor: Are you reporters?

Natalie: No, we are not reporters. We saw your drawings in a shop in Camden Market.

Lawrence Windsor: You recognised the drawings?

Natalie and Alice: Yes!

Lawrence Windsor: How is that possible?

Natalie: I am an art historian. I love Turner's work. When I saw the drawings in Robert Green's shop, I recognised them at once! We studied Turner extensively at university, so I can spot his work anywhere.

Lawrence Windsor: Are you also an art historian?

Alice: No. I am a writer.

Lawrence Windsor: What do you write about?

Alice: I write stories about mysteries, robberies, crime. I like solving mysteries.

Lawrence Windsor: Very good! Come in. Would you like something to drink?

14. THE REWARD

They are all sitting in the living room. Alice asks Mr. Lawrence Windsor some questions about the stolen drawings.

Alice: When did the robbery take place?

Lawrence Windsor: On Saturday, yesterday. I know because I saw the drawings on Friday night. Yesterday afternoon they were gone.

Alice: Did you call the police?

Lawrence Windsor: Of course, straight away.

Alice: Did you call the TV station as well?

Lawrence Windsor: Yes, I think it's best that everyone knows. That way, I can offer a reward.

Natalie: You are offering a reward to whoever finds the drawings?

Lawrence Windsor: Yes, of course. I am offering one thousand pounds as a reward! They announced it today on TV.

Alice: We don't care about your money, Mr. Windsor. We just want to help.

Natalie: It's true. We don't want any money. We just care about art.

Alice: And mysteries!

Natalie: And mysteries of course!

15. THE KEY

Lawrence tells Alice and Natalie everything about the robbery so that they can help him to get back the stolen drawings.

Alice: Where do you keep your art collection?

Lawrence Windsor: In a large room on the second floor, let's go up!

Alice: Does the door of the room have a lock?

Lawrence Windsor: Of course.

Alice: Who has the key to this room?

Lawrence Windsor: I have the key. No one else.

Alice: Where do you keep the key?

Lawrence Windsor: Here, on this golden chain that I always wear around my neck.

Natalie: Wow! What an amazing room. There are so many paintings!

Alice: Are you a big fan of art, Mr. Windsor?

Lawrence Windsor: Yes, more than anything in the world. Art is my life. I love my collection, and now I'm upset because it's incomplete.

16. THE INVESTIGATION

Alice asks Lawrence Windsor more questions while they look at the art collection.

Alice: Was the lock on the door broken?

Lawrence Windsor: No, the police say that nothing was broken.

Alice: So someone took the key.

Lawrence Windsor: Perhaps…. It would be tricky, but it's possible.

Alice: Who else lives here?

Lawrence Windsor: My daughter Mariana, my staff, and me.

Alice: How many staff do you have?

Lawrence Windsor: Six people: a cleaner, a security guard, a gardener, two cooks and my daughter's nanny. Do you think the thief is someone inside the house?

Alice: I don't know. It's possible. It's someone who doesn't know how much the drawings are worth. They were on sale in Camden Market for 100 pounds! But they must be worth thousands!

Lawrence Windsor: I really hope the thief isn't someone from inside the house!

17. THE INTERRUPTION

While Alice asks Lawrence Windsor some questions, a young girl enters the room. She is 12 years old, very tall and has blonde hair and dark brown eyes.

Lawrence Windsor: Mariana! Come here. I want to introduce you to these two charming women. This is Natalie, she is an art historian. She loves art, just like us.

Mariana Windsor: Hello, Natalie.

Natalie: Hello, Mariana, it's nice to meet you.

Lawrence Windsor: And this is Alice. She is a writer and knows a lot about robberies and mysteries.

Alice: Nice to meet you.

Mariana Windsor: And you.

Lawrence Windsor: They saw the drawings in Camden Market yesterday and now they are helping us to find them… and to catch the thief!

Mariana Windsor: Do you know who stole the drawings?!

Alice: No, not yet. But I am certain we are going to find out.

Mariana Windsor: Have you found any clues yet?

Alice: A few…. Wait, how did you get in? Do you have a key to this room as well?

Lawrence Windsor: Ah yes, I forgot to mention it. Mariana is the only other person who has a key.

18. LAWRENCE AND MARIANA

Alice and Natalie chat with Lawrence and Mariana about the disappearance of the drawings.

Alice: Did anyone ask you for the key, Mariana?

Mariana Windsor: No…. I always have it on me.

Lawrence Windsor: Mariana is very careful. She knows how important my art collection is. Isn't that right? She even has her own collection.

Mariana Windsor: Yes! I have a collection of comics.

Alice: Comics?

Mariana Windsor: Yes, comics and comic books! From all over the world; the United States, Japan, France, Argentina. I have both old and new ones.

Natalie: How interesting! I love comics. Can I see your collection?

Mariana Windsor: Yes, of course. Come with me. I'll show you.

19. THE SECOND COLLECTION

Mariana Windsor shows Natalie her collection of comic books. She has a large room with huge bookcases filled with comics.

Natalie: It's an amazing collection!

Mariana Windsor: Yes, it's my passion. I have been collecting comic books since I was five.

Natalie: Wow! It's amazing. Where do you buy them?

Mariana Windsor: I get the most common ones in comic bookshops. If they are rare comics, I buy them in antiques markets.

Natalie: You mean like the antiques market in Camden Market?

Mariana Windsor: Umm…. Yes, sometimes I buy them there. It's not too far from my house.

Natalie: Have you ever seen a man in a hat in Camden Market?

Mariana Windsor: Yes…. I think I know who you're talking about; a tall man in a black hat, right?

20. THE CLEANER

Alice and Lawrence Windsor go down to the living room to talk more about the staff, while Natalie stays in the room with Mariana.

Alice: I would like to talk some more about your staff. Is that okay?

Lawrence Windsor: Yes, of course. That's not a problem.

Alice: Who is the cleaner?

Lawrence Windsor: The cleaner is called Charlie. Charlie is Welsh and I have known him my whole life. His father was a friend of my father.

Alice: Do you think he could be the thief?

Lawrence Windsor: I don't think so. He's a good guy and I trust him a lot.

Alice: Okay. Did Charlie see anything strange that day?

Lawrence Windsor: Why don't you ask him? I'll call him down.

21. THE METAL BOX

While Natalie looks at Mariana's comic book collection, she sees a metal box that catches her eye.

Natalie: What's in that box?

Mariana Windsor: My most precious comic is in there. Do you want to see it?

Natalie: Yes, I would like to see it.

Mariana Windsor: Look….

Natalie: Oh! Is it very old?

Mariana Windsor: Yes, it's more than a hundred years old. It's from the United States. It's called *Little Nemo in Slumberland*.

Natalie: What is it about?

Mariana Windsor: It's about a boy who has strange dreams.

Natalie: Wow, I bet it's expensive. How much did it cost?

Mariana Windsor: Umm…. I don't know. I don't remember.

Natalie: How come you don't know? Did you buy it a long time ago?

Mariana Windsor: I think it's time to go back to my father.

22. CHARLIE

Lawrence Windsor calls Charlie down, the cleaner of the house. Charlie enters the room, where Alice and Lawrence are having tea. He sits with them, and Alice asks him questions about the day of the robbery.

Alice: Charlie, Mr. Windsor says you are Welsh.

Charlie: Yes, I'm from Cardiff!

Alice: Like my father. *Bore da!*

Charlie: Great! *Bore da.*

Alice: Okay, if you don't mind, let's talk about the day of the robbery. Did anything strange happen?

Charlie: It was yesterday, right?

Alice: Yes, it was yesterday, Saturday.

Charlie: Everything was normal; nothing out of the ordinary.... Except one thing.

Alice: What?

Charlie: When I was cleaning downstairs, I heard someone opening the coat wardrobe.

Alice: Why is that strange?

Charlie: Because it was so hot yesterday! Who needs a coat when it's so hot?

Alice: What time was that?

Charlie: At 10:30 in the morning....

23. THE GARDENER

Once Charlie leaves the room, Alice tells Lawrence Windsor what she thinks about Charlie.

Alice: He seems like a good guy! He's very smart.

Lawrence Windsor: Yes, he is a good guy. He is very intelligent.

Alice: Did you look for something in the coat wardrobe?

Lawrence Windsor: No, it wasn't me.

Alice: Now, tell me about the gardener. What's his name? Where is he from?

Lawrence Windsor: The gardener is called Artur. He's Polish. He is thirty years old. He hasn't been working here for long.

Alice: How long has he been working here, exactly?

Lawrence Windsor: He has been working here for six months. He is an excellent gardener. He looks after the plants very well. He loves his job.

Alice: Do you think the gardener could be the thief?

Lawrence Windsor: I don't think so. He seems trustworthy. He's a good person. Moreover, he almost never comes inside the house.

Alice: Great. Maybe he can tell us something helpful about the robbery.

Lawrence Windsor: I hope so! I'll call him.

24. ARTUR

The gardener, Artur, enters the room. Alice asks him several questions about the day of the robbery. Artur is tall and slim and has brown hair. He wears glasses, which are broken and have been stuck together with tape.

Alice: Good morning, Artur.

Artur: Good morning!

Alice: My name is Alice. I am investigating the robbery. Can I ask you some questions?

Artur: Sure! No problem. Are you a police officer?

Alice: No, I'm not a police officer. I'm just helping Mr. Windsor.

Artur: Very well. What would you like to know?

Alice: I just want to know if anything unusual happened in the house yesterday, the day of the robbery.

Artur: Hmm…. Yes, I think I saw something strange…. But I'm not sure.

Alice: Why aren't you sure?

Artur: See my glasses? They're broken! They broke yesterday morning while I was working. So I couldn't see very well.

Alice: What did you see?

Artur: It was a very hot and sunny day. However, around 10:30 in the morning I think I saw someone leave the house wearing a big coat and a hat.

Alice: A hat?!

Artur: Yes, I couldn't see very well, but I'm almost certain.

25. THE FIRST SUSPECT

Artur leaves the room and Alice tells Lawrence what she thinks about the person with the coat and the hat.

Lawrence Windsor: Why are you surprised by a person wearing a hat?

Alice: We saw a tall man wearing a hat in Robert Green's shop.

Lawrence Windsor: Really?

Alice: Yes! Do you know a tall man that always wears a hat?

Lawrence Windsor: Hmm…. No, no one comes to mind. Wait! Now I remember. There was a tall man wearing a hat near the house yesterday. But I think he is a reporter. Do you think he's the thief?

Alice: I don't know. But we saw a tall man in a hat in Robert Green's shop before the robbery.

Lawrence Windsor: Maybe it's the thief!

Alice: Yes, I think it could be.

26. THE COOKS

Then, Lawrence Windsor calls down the two cooks, Liz and Jacob, who are married. Both of them are around 60 years old. They have been working with Lawrence Windsor's family since they were young. They care for Lawrence a lot. He is like a son to them.

Liz: Good morning.

Alice: Hello! It's a pleasure to meet you.

Jacob: The pleasure is ours.

Alice: I would like to know if you saw something strange yesterday, on the day of the robbery, something out of the ordinary.

Liz: Hmm…. I don't think so. Everything was the same as usual. What do you think, Jacob?

Jacob: It was a very quiet day. We didn't cook anything until the evening.

Alice: No one ate before dinner?

Lawrence Windsor: I didn't have lunch at home because I went out to visit some friends.

Alice: And Mariana?

Liz: I spoke with Mariana at midday. She wasn't hungry. She was very excited about a new comic.... That girl loves

her comics! She reminds me of her father with his art collection.

Alice: Okay. One last question. Is it the first time that things have disappeared from the house?

Liz: No, come to think of it, it's not! Things have been disappearing a lot lately. Just a week ago, a beautiful and very valuable silver salt shaker disappeared....

27. THE DISCUSSION

Once Liz and Jacob leave the room, Alice asks Lawrence Windsor a few questions.

Alice: Liz and Jacob are a very nice couple.

Lawrence Windsor: Yes, they are part of the family. I care about them a lot.

Alice: Is it normal for Mariana to skip lunch?

Lawrence Windsor: Yes, sometimes she's not hungry, especially when she has a new comic book to read.

Alice: Do you buy her comics?

Lawrence Windsor: Yes, we always fight about it.

Alice: Why?

Lawrence Windsor: Because she always wants very expensive comic books. She spends a lot of money on them. I tell her to be more careful. I know her collection is important to her, but she's just a girl. She shouldn't spend so much money on comics.

Alice: Do you fight about it often?

Lawrence Windsor: Yes, a few days ago we had a big fight over a very expensive comic that she wanted to buy. It was far too much money for a comic if you ask me!

28. THE NANNY

Next, Lawrence Windsor calls down Mariana's nanny. The nanny is called Pauline. She is twenty years old. Her hair is black and curly and she has dark skin and green eyes.

Alice: Hi, Pauline. So, you are Mariana's nanny?

Pauline: Hi! Yes, I am.

Alice: Do you spend the whole day with her?

Pauline: During summer I usually spend all day with her. The rest of the year she spends most of the day at school. While she's at school, I go to university. I am studying teaching. One day I will be a teacher to lots of kids like Mariana!

Alice: That's great. What about on the weekends?

Pauline: On the weekends Mariana usually stays in her bedroom. She never wants to go out.

Alice: What does she do in there?

Pauline: She reads her comic books. She loves those comic books more than anything.

Alice: Did anything strange happen yesterday?

Pauline: I don't know! I wasn't home at all yesterday. I went to Oxford to visit my parents.

29. THE SECURITY GUARD

When Pauline leaves the room, Alice asks Lawrence some questions.

Alice: Pauline seems like a good nanny. But it is normal that Mariana is alone in the house, like she was yesterday?

Lawrence Windsor: Yes. Not often, but it does happen sometimes. Mariana is old enough to stay by herself. Moreover, our security guard is always at home, along with Liz, Jacob and the others.

Alice: Who is the security guard? What is his name? Where is he?

Lawrence Windsor: The security guard is called Daniel. He is Portuguese, but he speaks very good English.

Alice: How old is he?

Lawrence Windsor: He is around forty.

Alice: Has he worked here long?

Lawrence Windsor: Yes, he has worked here for five years.

Alice: Is he good at his job?

Lawrence Windsor: Yes, he's very good at his job. His main task is to control the security cameras. There has never been a robbery at the house... until yesterday!

30. DANIEL

Lawrence calls Daniel, the security guard, so that Alice can ask him some questions.

Alice: Hello! I have a few questions about yesterday, if that's not a problem.

Daniel: Sure. That's not a problem.

Alice: To start, did anything strange happen yesterday?

Daniel: I don't remember anything strange. I was watching the cameras all day. No one strange is seen entering the house in the video footage.

Alice: Does anyone else have a key, apart from the other employees?

Daniel: No. Only those who work here have a key, apart from Mr. Lawrence and the girl.

Alice: I see. Do you think we can see the recordings from the security cameras?

Daniel: Of course, no problem! I will get the tablet which has everything on it.

31. THE VIDEO FOOTAGE

Daniel looks for the tablet which has the video footage from the security cameras. The footage shows everyone who goes in and out of the house.

Alice: Did anyone leave the house on Friday night?

Daniel: No, no one leaves the house until Saturday morning.

Alice: Who was the first person to leave the house on Saturday?

Daniel: Pauline was the first person to leave. There she is. She leaves the house at around 9:00 in the morning.

Alice: She was going to Oxford to visit her parents.

Daniel: Then, at 10:00, Mr. Lawrence leaves.

Alice: He was going to visit some friends.

Lawrence Windsor: Exactly!

Daniel: Then, Charlie leaves at 10:30. You can't see his face, but that's his coat and hat… though I don't know why he was wearing a coat. It was so hot that day.

Alice: That's not Charlie! He was inside, cleaning.

Daniel: Really? Wait… let's look at the downstairs camera. You're right! There's Charlie, cleaning.

Lawrence Windsor: So who is the person leaving the house wearing a hat?

Alice: Someone who doesn't want to be seen by the cameras!

32. THE PERSON IN THE VIDEO FOOTAGE

Alice, Daniel and Lawrence Windsor look at the video footage of the security cameras from the day before. Someone leaves the house wearing a coat and hat. Their face can't be seen.

Alice: Let's carry on. Does anyone else leave the house?

Daniel: No. A while later, at 11am, the person in the hat returns to the house. It's someone who lives here! They have a key.

Alice: So it seems. Then who enters?

Daniel: Mr. Lawrence comes back around 2pm, and then Pauline returns at around 5pm.

Alice: Lawrence, what time did you realise that the drawings were missing?

Lawrence Windsor: Around six in the evening. I visit my collection every evening at that time. I immediately noticed something was wrong. The Turner drawings were missing!

Daniel: At 6:30pm you can see the police arriving at the house.

Alice: Look! There with the police... there is a man wearing a hat!

33. TWO HATS

Alice, Daniel and Lawrence Windsor continue to watch the video footage from the security cameras from the day before. They wonder who the man in the hat with the police is.

Lawrence Windsor: Do you think it's the same person who left the house, Alice?

Alice: I don't think so. This person is outside. The other person is inside. It can't be the same person.

Lawrence Windsor: Do you think there are two people in hats, then?

Alice: Yes, maybe. Look at the video recordings; the man with the hat is talking with the police.

Lawrence Windsor: Maybe he is a detective. Do you think he is a detective?

Alice: Yes, maybe. He looks a lot like the man in the hat who was in Robert Green's shop that morning…. I think it's the same person.

34. THE CONCLUSIONS

When Daniel leaves, Lawrence and Alice reflect on what they have discovered.

Alice: Okay, what do we know so far?

Lawrence Windsor: To start, we know that the drawings disappeared on Saturday morning.

Alice: Natalie and I saw the drawings in Robert Green's shop in Camden Market on Saturday around 11:30.

Lawrence Windsor: Camden Market is very close to the house. The person who took the drawings could have taken them, sold them in the shop and returned back to the house.

Alice: Only three people left the house on Saturday before 11am: you, Pauline and the mysterious person in the coat and hat.

Lawrence Windsor: That person took Charlie's coat and hat so that they could leave the house without their face being seen on the cameras.

35. NATALIE AND MARIANA WINDSOR RETURN

The door to the living room opens. It's Mariana and Natalie.

Lawrence Windsor: Hi, Darling. Did you show Natalie your comic book collection?

Mariana Windsor: Yes, Dad.

Natalie: Mariana has a beautiful collection…. It's very extensive.

Alice: Mariana, can I ask you a quick question?

Mariana Windsor: Yes.

Lawrence Windsor: Sure, go ahead.

Alice: Did you leave the house at any point yesterday?

Mariana Windsor: No, I didn't leave the house at all.

Alice: Okay. Did you hear anyone in the coat wardrobe?

Mariana Windsor: Umm… Yes! I think I heard someone take a coat and hat from there in the morning.

Alice: Great! Okay. Thanks, Mariana.

36. THE PROMISE

Natalie and Alice get up to go back to the hotel.

Lawrence Windsor: You're very kind, both of you. I hope we find the thief. Those works of art are very valuable. They are worth hundreds of thousands of pounds. And they are very important to me. They are my most prized possession.

Natalie: We are happy to help. Thank you for letting us be a part of this. Art is very important to me too.

Alice: I promise that we will do everything we can to find your stolen drawings, Mr. Windsor.

Lawrence Windsor: If you do, you'll receive a large reward.

Alice: That's not necessary. We're not doing it for the money.

Natalie: We'll be in touch. We'll let you know if we get any news.

Lawrence Windsor: Okay, thanks. Good luck!

37. ALICE TELLS NATALIE WHAT SHE KNOWS

When they leave the house, Alice tells Natalie everything she has found out.

Alice: I spoke with all the house staff.

Natalie: With all of them? Who are they?

Alice: There are six: Charlie, the cleaner; Artur, the gardener; Liz and Jacob, the cooks; Pauline, the nanny; and Daniel, the security guard.

Natalie: Okay. Do any of them seem suspicious?

Alice: No, none of them seem suspicious really. All of them are very nice. They answered all my questions.

Natalie: What did they tell you?

Alice: The security cameras show that the thief is someone from the house. Only three people came out of the house on Saturday: Lawrence Windsor, the nanny and someone who leaves wearing Charlie's coat and hat.

Natalie: Is it the man in the hat who was in the shop?

Alice: I don't think so. It's someone from inside the house who took the coat and hat from the wardrobe. Charlie and Mariana both confirmed that someone went in the coat wardrobe. They heard it.

Natalie: You already know a lot about the case. You're a good detective.

Alice: Thanks. What have you found out?

38. NATALIE TELLS ALICE WHAT SHE KNOWS

Natalie and Alice continue talking about what they know. They are walking by the fence, outside Lawrence Windsor's mansion.

Natalie: Mariana's comic collection is huge. You can tell that she loves comics just as much as her father loves the Turner drawings.

Alice: Don't you think that Mariana behaves a bit strangely?

Natalie: I agree. She does behave strangely. When I asked her about the cost of one of her comic books, she got awkward. Do you think we should call her a suspect?

Alice: I don't know. Maybe she knows something and doesn't want to say.

Natalie: Why do you think she isn't telling us everything she knows?

Alice: She could be protecting someone.

Natalie: Who? The thief?

Alice: It's possible. The thief is one of the three people seen on the cameras: the mysterious person, the nanny or even her father!

39. THERE HE IS AGAIN!

Just as they are getting further away from the house, Natalie can't believe what she sees....

Natalie: Alice, look! It's the man in the hat! It's the same man from Robert Green's shop!

Alice: It's true. It's him! In the video footage, that man can be seen with the police. Maybe he's a detective.

Natalie: He looks very suspicious to me. What is he doing here?

Alice: I don't know, but I want to find out. Let's go and talk to him.

Natalie: Are you crazy, Alice?

Alice: Let's go. He's getting further away! Run!

Natalie: You are definitely crazy....

Alice: He is running as well. I think he saw us. He is trying to get away.

Natalie: He is heading towards Camden Market. There are a lot of people and shops there. It will be difficult to find him....

40. FOLLOWING THE MAN IN THE HAT

Inside Camden Market, Natalie and Alice follow the man in the hat. He walks very quickly among people, stalls and shops.

Natalie: I don't see him. Do you?

Alice: No. I lost him. I know! Let's go to the terrace of this cafe. From up there we will able to see better.

Natalie: Are you sure? This is crazy....

Alice: Yes, let's go.

Natalie: You were right! From up here you can see the whole market.

Alice: Look, there he is!

Natalie: He is going down that alleyway.

Alice: Let's follow him!

41. THE ALLEYWAY

Alice and Natalie follow the man in the hat into an alleyway in Camden Market. In the alleyway, there are three shops and they don't know which one he has gone into. One is a watch shop, another is a furniture shop and the third is a bookshop.

Natalie: Where do you think he is?

Alice: He must be in one of these three shops. I am not sure which one he went into.

Natalie: Do you think he is in the watch shop?

Alice: No, I don't think he is inside the watch shop.

Natalie: Maybe he went into the furniture shop....

Alice: I don't think he's there either.

Natalie: So he must be in the bookshop.

Alice: Yes.... I think that's the most likely.

Natalie: Should we go inside and see?

Alice: Yes, let's look for him!

42. THE BOOKSHOP

Natalie and Alice go into the bookshop and, between the bookcases, they see the man in the hat sitting at a table and reading a book. He seems to be waiting for them.

Alice: There he is!

Man in the hat: Alice, Natalie, I've been waiting for you.

Natalie: How do you know our names?!

Man in the hat: I know many things….

Alice: What is your name?

Man in the hat: I can't tell you my name, yet.

Alice: Can we sit down?

Man in the hat: Yes, of course. Take a seat. We have a lot to talk about.

Alice: Are you following us?

Man in the hat: In fact, I believe it is you two who are following me.

Alice: Well… that's true. But only because you are always around when strange things happen.

Man in the hat: Strange things? Like what?

Alice: Like the robbery of the Turner drawings at Lawrence Windsor's mansion. And the robbery of the same drawings at Robert Green's shop.

43. FACE TO FACE WITH THE MAN IN THE HAT

Alice and Natalie talk to the man in the hat inside a bookshop in Camden Market.

Man in the hat: So you saw me that day in Robert Green's shop.

Alice: Yes, we saw you there. Then we saw you leave.

Man in the hat: Okay. I see that you are very observant.

Alice: We also saw you in Lawrence Windsor's house on the day of the robbery.

Man in the hat: Really? How?

Alice: On the security cameras. In the video footage, you are talking to the police.

Man in the hat: Yes, of course. It's true. You are very observant!

Natalie: Do you have anything to do with the robbery?

Man in the hat: I am not the thief, that's for sure.

Natalie: Are you a police officer?

Man in the hat: No, I'm not a police officer.

Natalie: Are you a detective, then?

Man in the hat: No, not exactly.

Alice: Then who are you?

44. THE HISTORIANS' CLUB

The man in the hat tells Alice and Natalie that he is part of a team of expert investigators that solve mysteries around the world.

Man in the hat: I am an investigator.

Natalie: And what do you investigate? Crimes? Robberies?

Man in the hat: Not exactly. I am part of a group.

Alice: A secret organisation?

Man in the hat: Yes, it's a secret organisation. We are called The Historians' Club.

Alice: What do you do?

Man in the hat: We solve mysteries.

Natalie: What kind of mystery?

Man in the hat: Well, we solve mysteries related to art history, archaeology and architecture.

Natalie: Like the theft of the Turner drawings!

Man in the hat: Exactly!

45. WHAT THE MAN IN THE HAT WAS DOING AT THE MARKET

Natalie and Alice share what they know about the man in the hat.

Alice: So, what do you know about the case?

Man in the hat: First I'd like to hear what you two know.

Alice: Okay.... To start, we know that someone took the Turner drawings from Lawrence Windsor's house on Saturday.

Man in the hat: At what time?

Alice: Before 11:30.

Man in the hat: How do you know?

Alice: Because at roughly 11:30, we saw the drawings in Robert Green's shop.

Man in the hat: Well done! I know, as I was also there....

Natalie: What were you doing there?

Man in the hat: Honestly, I was investigating some stolen art. There are lots of stolen works of art in Camden

Market. I wanted to see who was going to try and sell works of art in the shops, to try and catch some art thieves.

Natalie: So you overheard our conversation by chance?

Man in the hat: Absolutely! But I knew straight away that something fishy was going on....

46. WHAT THE MAN IN THE HAT DID NEXT

The man in the hat tells Natalie and Alice what he did on the day of the robbery.

Man in the hat: Yesterday, in Robert Green's shop, I overheard your conversation about the Turner drawings. Then I went to find out which museums and private collections in the city had original Turner drawings. It turns out there is a private collection with a number of drawings in a mansion not too far from Camden Market.

Natalie: Lawrence Windsor's collection!

Man in the hat: Exactly! I stayed near the house until the police came.

Alice: Do the police have any leads?

Man in the hat: No, they have no idea who did it. Who do you two think it was?

Alice: Don't forget that there could be two thieves! Someone took the drawings from the house.... But then someone stole them from Robert Green's shop.

Man in the hat: Exactly! You are very smart, Alice.

47. THE SUSPECTS

The man in the hat talks to Natalie and Alice about the suspects in the case.

Man in the hat: If there are indeed two thieves, I think we should focus on the first thief.

Alice: We are almost certain that the first thief was someone from the house. On the security cameras you can see that the only people who leave the house are Lawrence Windsor, the nanny and someone else....

Man in the hat: Someone else?

Alice: Yes, someone covered up in a hat and a coat. Their face can't be seen in the video footage.

Man in the hat: Is it a man or a woman?

Alice: We don't know!

Man in the hat: What time do they leave the house?

Alice: At 10:30.

Man in the hat: And do they come back later?

Alice: Yes, they return at 11.

Man in the hat: So the first thief is definitely someone from the house!

Alice: Yes, but who?

48. THE MAN IN THE HAT DISAPPEARS

Natalie and Alice talk to the man in the hat in the bookshop. However, while they are talking, a sudden loud noise from behind makes Natalie and Alice turn around. Several books have fallen off the shelves. When they turn back, the man in the hat is gone!

Natalie: Where has the man in the hat gone? He was sat here a second ago.

Alice: He disappeared! As if by magic!

Natalie: And who knocked those books down behind us? They scared the life out of me....

Alice: I don't know. Maybe someone was spying on us from behind the bookcase.

Natalie: That's scary!

Alice: Yes, this is a very strange case. Look at this....

Natalie: The book that the man in the hat was reading when we arrived; what's special about it?

Alice: It's not just any book, it's a comic!

49. PAULINE AT THE MARKET

Natalie and Alice leave the bookshop.

Natalie: Shall we go back to the hotel? It's getting late Maybe we can carry on investigating tomorrow morning.

Alice: The life of a detective is exhausting!

Natalie: Hey, look who's over there!

Alice: It's Pauline, Mariana's nanny!

Natalie: Yes, do you think she comes to the market often?

Alice: Hmm…. I don't know, let's ask the seller. Excuse me, have you seen that woman around here before?

Seller: Pauline? Yes, of course. She is always around here.

Alice: Does she buy a lot of antiques?

Seller: Well… to be honest, I don't think so. I've never seen her buy anything.

Alice: Thanks for your help.

Natalie: It's a bit suspicious, don't you think?

Alice: Yes, I think it's quite suspicious….

50. BACK IN ROBERT GREEN'S SHOP

Natalie and Alice are very surprised to see Pauline in Camden Market.

Natalie: It's possible that Pauline comes here just because she likes antiques.

Alice: Yeah, of course. That doesn't necessarily make her the thief.

Natalie: Also, Robert Green said that the person who brought him the drawings was a man....

Alice: That's true. Maybe we could go and ask him before going back to the hotel.... If you don't mind.

Natalie: Of course! I'm tired, but I don't mind a slight detour.... Since we're already here.

Alice: You're great, Natalie! Thanks.

Natalie: No need to thank me, Alice. It's been a lot of fun investigating this mystery with you. Let's go!

Alice: Look, the shop windows are still broken. There's Robert Green. Should we go in?

Natalie: Yes, let's.

Robert Green: Hi! How are you both?

Alice: Good, thanks. We don't want to bother you. We just wanted to ask you again about the person who brought you the Turner drawings.

Robert Green: Ah yes, that mysterious young woman….

Alice: Woman?! Didn't you say before that it was a man?

51. THE MEMORY

Robert Green accidentally says that the person who brought the Turner drawings to the shop was a woman, not a man.

Natalie: Didn't you say that it was a man that brought you the drawings? A mysterious man?

Alice: Yes, you did. I remember perfectly! You never mentioned a woman....

Robert Green: That's right.... I did say it was a man. But now I remember. It wasn't a man who brought me the Turner drawings. It was a woman!

Alice: Why did you say it was a man?

Robert Green: My memory is very poor.... I couldn't remember very well.

Alice: Hmm.... And now you remember?

Robert Green: Yes, now I remember. It was a woman.

Alice: Was it a woman with black curly hair and green eyes by any chance?

Robert Green: Hmm.... Yes, it was! Now I remember; it was a woman with black curly hair and green eyes.

52. NATALIE AND ALICE HAVE DOUBTS ABOUT ROBERT GREEN

Alice and Natalie leave Robert Green's shop and take two city bikes to go to the hotel. While they ride, they talk about their doubts.

Alice: There's something strange about Robert Green's behaviour, don't you think?

Natalie: Yes, definitely.

Alice: I don't think he's being completely honest with us.

Natalie: Do you think he's lying?

Alice: He could be lying.

Natalie: Do you think he's the thief?

Alice: No, I don't think he's the thief. The thief must be someone from the house. It can't be Robert Green.

Natalie: But perhaps he made a deal with someone in the house.

Alice: But then why would he be selling Turner's works at such a low price?

Natalie: That's true. Even so, I think he's lying. He's hiding something.

Alice: I agree! Something suspicious is going on.

Natalie: But everything points to Pauline being the thief....

Alice: Yes, we have to find a way to prove it.

53. IN THE PUB

Natalie and Alice go to a pub in an area called Covent Garden. There they talk about the case.

Waiter: Good evening, what can I get you?

Alice: I am so hungry! I think I'll have the shepherd's pie.

Waiter: Would you like the same?

Natalie: No, no, I'm not that hungry. I'll just have a portion of chips.

Waiter: Okay, I'll bring you your food in a few minutes!

Natalie: Thanks!

Alice: Okay, now we can sit calmly and think.

Natalie: What are your thoughts?

Alice: Well, we suspect that Pauline could be the thief, but we are not sure. There is also the mysterious person who leaves the house wearing a coat and hat. He, or she, could also be the thief.

Natalie: What can we do to find out whether Pauline is guilty or innocent?

54. THE PLAN

In the pub, Natalie and Alice look for a way to prove whether Pauline is the one who stole the Turner drawings.

Alice: I have an idea! It's something that usually works in police crime novels. Tomorrow we'll go to Lawrence Windsor's house. We'll ask him to gather together everyone in the house.

Natalie: Okay.... Then what?

Alice: Once everyone is there, we will tell them what we know.

Natalie: What do we know?

Alice: First, we'll tell them that we know the thief is someone in the house. Then, we'll tell them Robert Green remembered that the person who brought the Turner drawings to his shop was a woman, not a man....

Natalie: Okay, what else?

Alice: We'll tell them that Robert Green remembers the person's face perfectly. Then we'll tell them that we will call him and ask him to tell us who the thief is... unless that person wants to confess everything.

Natalie: Do you think that will work? And what if it doesn't?

Alice: If no one says anything, we'll call Robert Green to see what he says….

Waiter: Excuse me, here is your food. Enjoy!

Alice and Natalie: Great! Thanks.

55. BACK IN THE WINDSOR'S HOUSE

The next day, Natalie and Alice go to the Windsor's house once more.

Lawrence Windsor: Hello! Nice to see you again.

Alice: Hello, Mr. Windsor! You too.

Lawrence Windsor: Shall we go into the living room?

Natalie: Sure!

Alice: Mr. Windsor, we have come because we have a plan. We think we know who the thief is. It's someone in the house!

Lawrence Windsor: Yes, I thought it might be, but who?

Alice: That's what the plan is for, to confirm whether it's the person we think it is.

Lawrence Windsor: Okay, what do we need to do?

Natalie: You need to call everyone in the house. We'll gather here in the living room.

56. THE TEST

Charlie (the cleaner), Artur (the gardener), Liz and Jacob (the cooks), Daniel (the security guard), Pauline (the nanny) and Mariana Windsor come down to the living room. Everyone greets Natalie and Alice and then they sit down.

Liz: What's going on? Have you discovered something about the robbery?

Daniel: Do you know who it was that left the house in the hat and coat?

Charlie: With my hat and coat. I didn't leave the house all Saturday!

Artur: Do you know where the Turner drawings are?

Lawrence Windsor: Okay, calm down everyone. Natalie and Alice have discovered a few things about the case. If we let them speak, they'll tell us what they know.

Alice: That's right. We know that the thief is someone in the house.

Jacob: No! That's impossible!

Alice: Yes, it's someone from inside the house…. Someone here in this room!

Charlie: How do you know?

Natalie: The owner of the antiques shop where the drawings were found told us who took them....

57. CRYING

When Natalie says that they know who the thief is, Mariana Windsor begins to cry uncontrollably!

Mariana Windsor: Okay, I admit it! I confess! It was me!

All: WHAT!?

Mariana Windsor: Yes, I stole the drawings. I took Charlie's coat and hat to hide from the cameras, and I took them to Robert Green's shop.

Lawrence Windsor: Mariana, what are you talking about? You're the thief?

Mariana Windsor: I'm sorry, Dad. I'm so ashamed! I didn't want to cause any trouble.

Lawrence Windsor: But why?

Mariana Windsor: I will tell you everything… A few months ago, we started arguing over money. I wanted to buy more comics for my collection, but you said I was spending too much. I always bought my comics at Camden Market. I used to go with Pauline in the afternoon.

Natalie: That's why the market sellers said they always see Pauline, even though she never buys anything.

58. MARIANA'S CONFESSION

Mariana has confessed that she took the Turner drawings from the house. She is explaining why she did it to her father, Alice, Natalie and all the house staff.

Pauline: Of course, I just take Mariana there! I'm not interested in antiques. She always goes to buy her comics and I stay nearby, looking at the old objects for sale.

Alice: That makes sense! We were worried that Pauline was involved in the robbery.

Pauline: Of course not! I would never steal from my boss. I love my job....

Lawrence Windsor: Carry on, Mariana.

Mariana Windsor: I would almost always buy comics in Robert Green's shop, but he started to charge me more and more for the comic books. When I told him that my father didn't want to give me any more money to buy comics, he told me I could bring him a valuable object from the house....

Alice: What? Robert Green told you to steal from your father?

59. THE TRADE-OFF

Mariana Windsor explains that she stole the Turner drawings because she needed more money to buy comics for her collection. When her father stopped giving her money, Robert Green told her she could take him valuable objects from the house in exchange....

Mariana Windsor: No! He didn't ask me to steal. He told me that he made lots of trade-offs with his customers.

Natalie: Trade-offs?

Mariana Windsor: Yes, a trade-off, an exchange. He would give me a valuable object if I gave him one.

Alice: So you took him the drawings?

Mariana Windsor: No, that was much later. First, I began to take him small objects, things that I found around the house.

Alice: Like what?

Mariana Windsor: I don't know, a book from the library, a watch, an old salt shaker....

Liz: You took the silver salt shaker!

Mariana Windsor: I'm sorry! I wasn't thinking!

60. LITTLE NEMO

Mariana tells everyone about the trade-offs she made with Robert Green. One day, a very valuable comic arrives at the shop and Mariana must bring him something very valuable in exchange.

Mariana Windsor: Then, one day, a very special comic arrived at the shop....

Natalie: *Little Nemo in Slumberland.*

Mariana Windsor: Exactly. An original edition, in English, signed by the author! I had to have it. Robert Green saved it specially for me.

Lawrence Windsor: Was it the time that you asked me for a hundred pounds to buy a comic?

Mariana Windsor: Yes! But obviously you didn't give me the money. I was so angry. I needed to get that comic book.

Alice: So then what happened?

Mariana Windsor: I took various things to the shop to trade, but nothing was good enough for Mr. Green. He said that I had to take him something more valuable. So then I decided to take something from my father's art collection....

61. MARIANA, REGRETFUL

Mariana explains the details of how she took the works of art from her father's collection.

Lawrence Windsor: I can't believe it!

Mariana Windsor: I'm sorry, Dad. I really regret it. On that day, in the morning, I took advantage of the fact that Pauline had left the house. Then you left too. I took the key to the art collection and opened the door. Then, I took the drawings because I knew they were valuable, but I didn't know how much they were worth. I even thought you might not notice, because you already have so many in your collection....

Lawrence Windsor: Of course I noticed! I noticed immediately. Those drawings are worth hundreds of thousands of pounds. They are the most valuable items in my collection!

Mariana Windsor: I know that now. I didn't know they were so valuable.... They were just drawings, so I thought they wouldn't be much more expensive than an old comic book. After grabbing the drawings, I took Charlie's coat and hat so that Daniel wouldn't see me on the security cameras.

62. MARIANA'S PLEA TO ROBERT GREEN

As well as revealing how she stole the drawings, Mariana explains to Alice, Natalie and her father why Robert Green didn't say anything.

Mariana Windsor: I took everything to Robert Green's shop. He was so happy with the drawings, and he gave me *Little Nemo* in exchange.

Alice: Mariana, why didn't Robert Green tell us it was you? First, he said it was a man; then, that it was a woman with black hair and green eyes like Pauline. Why did he lie?

Mariana Windsor: That's my fault as well! After all the drama about the robbery, I asked Pauline if we could go to Camden Market for a bit. I went to Robert Green's shop and begged him not to say anything.

Pauline: It's true, we went in the afternoon.

Natalie: Yes, we saw you there.

Mariana Windsor: I saw you two as well, in a bookshop, talking to a man in a hat.

Alice: It was you spying on us in the shop!

Mariana Windsor: I just wanted to know if you suspected me. I'm sorry. I'm so sorry!

63. FORGIVENESS

While Mariana cries uncontrollably, Lawrence Windsor assures his daughter that there's nothing to worry about.

Lawrence Windsor: Mariana, it's not your fault. You made a mistake.... A big one. But I know you didn't mean to hurt me. You didn't think about the consequences. Don't cry, everything's okay.

Alice: It's true, Mariana. The only thing that matters now is finding the second thief so we can get the works back.

Lawrence Windsor: And if we don't get them back, it doesn't change anything. I'll always love you.

Mariana Windsor: Thanks, Dad. I love you too. Does that mean you forgive me?

Lawrence Windsor: Of course I forgive you.

Alice: Okay, now we have to find out who took the drawings from Robert Green's shop.

Lawrence Windsor: There is something strange about that man.

Alice: Well, he did lie to us. I think we should talk to him again.

Lawrence Windsor: Yes, though this time, I think you should go with the police....

64. THE POLICE

Lawrence Windsor gives Alice and Natalie a small card with a telephone number on.

Alice: Whose number is this?

Lawrence Windsor: It's the number of Detective Smith.

Alice: The police officer who's investigating the case?

Lawrence Windsor: Yes, she is the police officer in charge of the case regarding the robbery.

Alice: We should call her.

Lawrence Windsor: Yes, I think you should. I think the three of you could work well together.

Natalie: That sounds like a great idea!

Lawrence Windsor: With Detective Smith, you can question Robert Green again and ask him why he didn't tell you the truth. Maybe if you go with the police, he'll tell the truth.

65. THE TELEPHONE CALL

Alice and Natalie telephone Detective Smith and ask her to investigate the robbery of the Turner drawings together.

Detective Smith: Hello?

Natalie: Hello, Detective Smith. Do you remember me? My name is Natalie.

Detective Smith: Ah, Natalie! I assume you are with Alice, investigating the robbery of the Turner drawings.

Natalie: Yes! How did you know?

Detective Smith: It's my job to know these things! I am investigating everything related to the robbery as well. I know you are doing the same.

Natalie: Yes, we have been making some inquiries…. We don't want to interfere with the police, of course.

Detective Smith: No, it's not a problem. Why are you calling?

Natalie: If possible, Detective, we would like to meet with you. We have some information that we think could help and you could also help us to move forward with the investigation.

66. THE MEETING IN THE SQUARE

Alice and Natalie make plans to meet with Detective Smith in Trafalgar Square, London. Detective Smith is a woman in her forties. She is tall, with brown hair and dark brown eyes. She wears red glasses.

Detective Smith: Hi Natalie, hi Alice.

Natalie: Hi, Detective. It's a pleasure to meet you.

Detective Smith: The pleasure is mine! Now tell me, what have you found out so far?

Alice: This is what we know so far; Mariana, the daughter of Lawrence Windsor, has a collection of comics that are very important to her. She normally buys them in Camden Market, and for a while now she has been buying them in Robert Green's shop, but her father stopped giving her money for the comics. That's when she started to steal objects from the house to exchange for comic books at the shop.

Detective Smith: Robert Green told the girl to steal?

Alice: Mariana says he didn't. He only told her that he could do a trade-off, but he didn't specifically tell her to steal.

67. THE PLAN WITH DETECTIVE SMITH

Natalie and Alice tell Detective Smith everything they know so far about the robbery of the Turner drawings.

Detective Smith: What do you know about the second robbery?

Alice: Not a lot. We know that when we saw the drawings and recognised them, Robert Green called a friend of his… an art expert, to ask him to go and see them the next day.

Detective Smith: And then what?

Alice: Then, someone smashed the shop windows that night and stole the drawings.

Detective Smith: It wasn't either of you, was it?

Natalie: Ha ha ha.

Alice: No, no, of course not.

Detective Smith: Okay, I had to ask. It's my job.

Natalie: We just want the drawings back in Lawrence Windsor's collection, where they will be safe and well looked after.

Detective Smith: I see. Let's make a plan.

Alice: Okay, what shall we do next?

Detective Smith: We need to go back to Robert Green's shop. There is something that we're missing....

68. THE INTERROGATION

Natalie, Alice and Detective Smith go to speak with Robert Green in his shop. Detective Smith shows him a photo of Mariana Windsor on her mobile phone.

Detective Smith: Please look at this photo, Mr. Green. Do you recognise this girl?

Robert Green: Yes, yes, I recognise her.

Detective Smith: Do you know her name?

Robert Green: Yes, it's the girl from the Windsor mansion.... Mariana.

Detective Smith: Okay. How do you know her?

Robert Green: She often comes to the shop to buy comics.

Detective Smith: Mr. Green, did this girl bring you the Turner drawings?

Robert Green: Yes, it was her.

Alice: Why didn't you say so before?

Robert Green: I know it's bad to lie, really. But she begged me not to say anything. She's just a girl. I couldn't betray her trust like that. She's been coming to the shop for years. She is one of my best customers. She trusts me. She asked me not to tell anyone who brought the drawings. I decided to keep it a secret for her.

Detective Smith: Did you know that the objects she brought in were stolen?

Robert Green: Of course not! I had no idea.

69. A NEW SUSPECT

Detective Smith, Alice and Natalie continue to ask Robert Green questions in order to find the second thief.

Detective Smith: Mr. Green, who knew that the Turner drawings were here? Did you tell anyone?

Robert Green: Hmm… let me think. Well, apart from myself and these two women, I don't think there's anyone else …

Natalie: What about your friend?

Robert Green: What friend?

Natalie: The British art historian.

Detective Smith: What are you talking about?

Natalie: When we recognised the drawings, Mr. Green called his friend, an art historian, to have him confirm that the drawings were indeed Turner originals. He was going to come to the shop the next day.

Detective Smith: Who is the art historian, Mr. Green?

Robert Green: His name is Michael Wright.

Detective Smith: Can we talk to him?

70. THE SEARCH FOR MICHAEL WRIGHT

Mr. Robert Green gives Detective Smith information about Michael Wright, his address and telephone number. Then, the three of them leave the shop.

Alice: What do you think, Detective Smith?

Detective Smith: I think we should talk with Michael Wright. Maybe he's the person we are looking for. Let's call his house… I'll call him right now.

Natalie: No one answered?

Detective Smith: No. It rang, but no one picked up.

Natalie: Shall we try his mobile?

Detective Smith: Okay, I'll call his mobile.

Alice: Did it ring?

Detective Smith: No. His phone must be off.

Natalie: That seems suspicious.

Detective Smith: Yes, it is strange.

Alice: Should we go to his house to talk to him?

Detective Smith: Yes! Do you want to come?

Alice: Definitely, let's go!

Natalie: Let's go!

71. THE LAST LOCATION

Detective Smith takes Natalie and Alice to the address that Robert Green gave them. They ring the doorbell, but no one comes to the door. Meanwhile, Smith asks her colleagues to confirm that the address and telephone number are correct.

Detective Smith: This is the address of Michael Wright, Doctor in Art History, specialist in British art.

Alice: How weird! Right? He doesn't answer the phone, there's no one home, and his mobile is turned off.

Detective Smith: Yes, it is strange. I've asked my colleagues to try and find out the location of his mobile phone.

Natalie: They can do that?

Detective Smith: Yes, if the GPS has been used recently, they can locate the phone. They've found it! They say that the mobile phone was detected in Newcastle a few hours ago.

Alice: Newcastle? That's five hours away... What is he doing there?

Natalie: I think I know what he might be doing there....

Detective Smith: What?

Natalie: There is a big art festival that begins today in Newcastle. Art collectors visit from all around the world.

Alice: So that means....

Detective Smith: That means that if he has the Turner drawings, he can sell them there....

72. THE TRIP TO NEWCASTLE

Alice, Natalie and Detective Smith have suspicions about Michael Wright, who appears to be in Newcastle.

Detective Smith: Okay. The next step is to travel to Newcastle. We have to prevent the drawings from being sold on the black market.

Alice: Also… there is a ferry port in Newcastle.

Natalie: So if he manages to sell the works, he can get a ferry to Holland and leave the country.

Detective Smith: Exactly. We have to leave as soon as possible. I understand if you prefer to stay here and enjoy your holiday.

Alice: Are you joking, Detective Smith?! We wouldn't miss this for the world!

Detective Smith: Ha ha ha. Okay, get in the car then, because we're leaving right now!

Natalie: This plan is crazy!

Alice: If you want to stay, I get it….

Natalie: No, of course not! This is a crazy plan… that I want to be part of!

Detective Smith: Okay then, say no more.

73. THE NEWCASTLE ARTS FESTIVAL

Detective Smith, Alice and Natalie travel to the city of Newcastle, just 30 minutes from the East coast, in Detective Smith's car. The Newcastle arts festival is filled with visitors, collectors and artists. There are hundreds of people.

Alice: How are we going to find this man among all these people?

Detective Smith: I have a photo of him! My colleagues at the police station sent it to me. Look!

Natalie: He's an older man. He must be around sixty.

Detective Smith: Sixty-two, according to the report they sent me.

Alice: He has long, grey hair and wears glasses with a gold frame.

Natalie: That helps. It won't be very difficult to find him.

Detective Smith: We can split up. Natalie, you go right. Alice, you go left. I'll go down the centre.

Alice: Perfect.

Natalie: Let's go!

74. THE CHASE

Detective Smith, Alice and Natalie split up to look for Michael Wright at the Newcastle arts festival.

Natalie: Alice, Alice! I saw him! He is carrying a briefcase. I think he went that way!

Detective Smith: Did you see anything?

Alice: Yes, Natalie said she saw him go that way. He is carrying a briefcase!

Detective Smith: Perfect, let's go that way.

Natalie: Look! There he is.

Alice: I don't see him. Where is he?

Natalie: He's the man in the purple suit.

Detective Smith: There he is, going up the staircase.

Alice: I see him. How do we stop him?

Detective Smith: Alice, you go up that staircase. I'll go up this one. Natalie, you stay here in case he comes back down.

Natalie: Okay!

75. MICHAEL WRIGHT

Detective Smith and Alice run towards the man, each one from a different direction. When they get closer, running directly towards him, the man sees them, is startled and drops the briefcase, which falls open. Inside is....

Alice: A banana?

Detective Smith: What's that? A banana?

Michael Wright: Who are you? What do you want? Yes, it's my snack. What's the problem?

Detective Smith: I'm sorry, Mr. Wright. I'm Detective Smith. We've come from London. Can we talk to you?

Michael Wright: Yes, of course. Is something wrong?

Detective Smith: That's what we're trying to find out....

Michael Wright: What's going on?

Detective Smith: We have been trying to get in touch with you since this morning. We went to your house and called your phone, but there was no answer.

Michael Wright: Well, no. I'm clearly not at home. I'm here on holiday.... And my mobile battery ran out a few hours ago. Is there a problem with that?

Detective Smith: No, of course not. Can you tell us if you know a man called Robert Green?

76. MICHAEL'S STORY

Michael Wright, at the Newcastle arts festival, answers Detective Smith, Alice and Natalie's questions.

Michael Wright: Yes, I know Robert Green. He's not a close friend, but I know who he is. He's that man who sells stolen objects in his shop in Camden Market, right? Has something happened to him?

Detective Smith: Have you spoken with him recently?

Michael Wright: No. I haven't spoken to him in more than a year. Why?

Detective Smith: He didn't call you last Saturday to ask you to go to his shop and see original Turner drawings?

Michael Wright: Ha ha ha. Of course not! If I knew there were original Turner drawings in Camden Market, I wouldn't be here in Newcastle…. I'd be in Camden Market.

Detective Smith: He said he called you to talk about the authenticity of the drawings.

Michael Wright: Absolutely not. He never called.

Alice: But he made the call in front of us.

Michael Wright: Well that liar must have faked it. I haven't received any calls.

77. THE NON-EXISTENT CALL

Detective Smith contacts the police headquarters in London to confirm whether Robert Green made any calls to Michael Wright.

Detective Smith: It seems that Robert Green hasn't made any calls!

Natalie: Really?

Detective Smith: They have confirmed it at the police station in London. They traced his mobile phone records and it turns out that he didn't make any calls that day.

Michael Wright: That's precisely what I told you. I haven't received any calls.

Detective Smith: How long have you known Robert Green?

Michael Wright: I have known him for a few years. I would go to his shop in Camden Market sometimes to see the antiques....

Detective Smith: But you are not friends?

Michael Wright: No, definitely not. He's just a man I would occasionally buy things from. But, as I said, I haven't spoken to him in over a year....

Detective Smith: Why?

Michael Wright: Well, to be honest, I don't like his business very much.

Detective Smith: Why not?

Michael Wright: Because he has a lot of stolen objects!

78. THE DECEIT

Detective Smith finishes questioning Michael Wright and, after checking his briefcase, lets him go. Then she talks with Alice and Natalie about what they should do next.

Detective Smith: What do you both think?

Alice: I think it's obvious that Michael Wright has nothing to do with this. We've been deceived!

Natalie: We've been tricked by Robert Green. And it's not the first time he's lied to us! He must have known that Michael Wright comes to this arts festival every year. He used it to get us out of the city.

Alice: Do you think it's possible to arrest Robert Green, Detective Smith?

Detective Smith: We don't have any evidence yet. Even if he has lied, we can't arrest him just for that. We have to catch him 'red-handed'. We have to find the Turner drawings.

Alice: But what if he's escaping right now, taking advantage of us being here in Newcastle?

Detective Smith: I will call the police station in London and have them watch over him. They will make sure he doesn't escape. If he tries to get away with the drawings, we will arrest him.

Natalie: Should we go, then?

Detective Smith: Let's go!

79. THE RETURN TRIP

On the trip back to London, Detective Smith asks Natalie to give her more information about the drawings.

Detective Smith: If we do find Robert Green with the Turner drawings, we have to make sure that they are actually the ones we are looking for. Can you describe the drawings?

Natalie: Of course. There are three drawings.

Detective Smith: Are they large?

Natalie: No, they're not very big. They can easily fit inside a briefcase.

Detective Smith: Okay, what else?

Natalie: The paper is very old. It's a yellowish colour, not white.

Detective Smith: Great, what are the drawings of?

Natalie: One of the drawings is of a large church.

Detective Smith: A church?

Natalie: Yes, a large church with a cemetery in front.

Detective Smith: Okay, what about the other two drawings?

Natalie: Another drawing shows a sleeping cat curled up in a ball.

Detective Smith: Great, and the third drawing?

Natalie: The third drawing is of a ship in rough seas, looking like it's about to capsize.

Detective Smith: Okay, good to know.

80. THE ESCAPE

A few hours later, Alice, Natalie and Detective Smith arrive in London. It's early morning. The sun is coming up and the streets begin to fill with Londoners going to work. The women go directly to Robert Green's shop.

Detective Smith: That police car is making sure that Robert Green doesn't escape. Let's ask my colleagues if they have seen anything strange.

Alice: Okay!

Detective Smith: Hello Officer Gupta. This is Alice and Natalie. They are helping with the investigation. How is everything going? Have you seen him?

Officer Gupta: Hi, Detective Smith. Good morning. Mr. Green is in the flat above the shop. He's been there since last night. He turned off the lights a few hours ago. We are waiting on some kind of movement.

Natalie: Look! He's coming out of the flat.

Detective Smith: He's got a briefcase. Let's go. Mr. Green, stop!

Alice: He's running away! We have to catch him!

Detective Smith: Turn on the flashing lights in the police car, Gupta.

Officer Gupta: He's gone down that narrow alleyway. We can't drive down there.

Detective Smith: Let's run after him!

81. THE CHASE

Natalie, Alice and Detective Smith run after Robert Green as the police car cannot fit in the alleyway he has gone down.

Alice: This alleyway is so dark!

Natalie: I can't see anything. Do you think he's hiding somewhere?

Alice: I can hear him breathing.

Detective Smith: Wait. Let me turn my torch on.

Alice: Much better! There, behind those rubbish bins, something is moving!

Detective Smith: Quiet! I'm going to sneak up....

Cat: MEOWWWW!

Alice and Natalie: AAAAAHHHHH!

Detective Smith: Calm down, it was just a cat! But where has Robert Green gone?

Alice: There he is, at the other end

Detective Smith: Let's go!

Natalie: He's a fast runner!

Alice: He turned left!

Detective Smith: There are lots of winding streets around here. He wants us to lose sight of him. Let's split up again. Natalie, you go right. Alice, you go left. I'll go straight. I don't think he's dangerous, but if he has a gun you should get down on the ground.

Natalie: A gun?! But he's just an ordinary thief....

Detective Smith: Natalie, you never know what people are capable of doing for money!

82. THE BICYCLES

The three of them start running in different directions. In the early morning silence, Robert Green's footsteps can be heard not too far away. Nonetheless, one minute later, the three women find themselves back facing each other at a crossroads.

Natalie: Damn! Where did he go?

Alice: There he is. He flagged down a cab. Look!

Detective Smith: Yes, that's him. If he gets in that car, we won't be able to catch him.

Natalie: Unless we find our own vehicles to follow him.

Detective Smith: How? The police car is back by the shop. We will lose sight of him.

Natalie: Well, how about those?

Alice: The city bikes! Let's go!

Detective Smith: Have you got your travel cards to hand?

Alice and Natalie: Always!

Detective Smith: Okay, let's go!

Alice: How exciting! I feel like I'm in one of my novels....

Natalie: This is terrifying! I feel like I'm in one of your novels....

Detective Smith: Right, these are electric bikes, if we want to catch him, we must increase the speed as high as it will go, ready?

Alice: Yes!

Natalie: No!

Detective Smith: Let's go!

83. THE FALL

The three of them set the bikes at maximum speed, which proceed to shoot off towards the car, and they manage to catch up with it in just a few seconds. Detective Smith rides in front. As she is about to reach the cab, however, Robert Green opens the door and Detective Smith slams into it with force. She falls down in the middle of the street next to her bike. Natalie and Alice stop to help her.

Detective Smith: What are you doing? Keep going!

Natalie: Are you okay?

Detective Smith: Yes, it's just a scratch. Go!

Alice: Ok!

Natalie: He's stopped at the traffic lights! Let's go.

Alice: Careful when you get close, stay away from the doors.

Robert Green: Don't come any closer! I won't give you anything.

Alice: Stop this madness, Mr. Green. The police will stop you anyway.

Robert Green: Not if I can help it!

Natalie: The traffic lights have turned green. He's getting away!

Alice: And if we catch up with him, what do we do? We need to think of a plan.

84. THE PLAN

As they ride behind the cab, Natalie and Alice come up with a simple plan to get the briefcase back. There are more and more vehicles on the road.

Alice: Okay, the window on the left-hand side is open. We can get close to him that way.

Natalie: Do you think there's enough space to take the briefcase out?

Alice: No, no, we'll just get close enough to talk to him. One of us should do that. The other should approach the other side of the car, on the right. I doubt he has locked the door after he opened it to knock down Detective Smith.

Natalie: Okay, once we have opened the door, then what?

Alice: Once we open the door, we sneak inside the car and take the briefcase without him noticing!

Natalie: What?! You can do that bit! I'm not stepping foot inside that car with that maniac inside!

Alice: Okay, well then you have to be the one who distracts him.

Natalie: Right. I'll have to think of a distraction....

85. THE DISTRACTION

The car arrives on Regents Street, where it is about to make a stop at traffic lights. The women take advantage of the opportunity. Natalie goes first, approaching the left-hand side of the vehicle, where the window is wound down.

Robert Green: Get away! You don't want to get hurt....

Cab driver: He's right, you should keep some distance so as to prevent causing an accident.

Robert Green: Shut up!

Cab driver: How rude!

Natalie: Mr. Green, you have to give back the briefcase. Sooner or later they will catch you.

Robert Green: Catch me? What for? I haven't done anything. This briefcase belongs to me.

Natalie: I'm not talking about the briefcase; I'm talking about what's inside!

Robert Green: I acquired what's inside legally. The girl brought it to my shop and I exchanged it for an extremely valuable comic book that's over one hundred years old. When I make a good business deal, why should I have to give away my profits?

Cab driver: What is she doing by the other door?

Robert Green: HEY! WHAT'S GOING ON?!

86. THE ARGUMENT

While Robert Green talks to Natalie, Alice tries to slowly sneak into the cab on the right side, until the driver sees her. Then, Robert Green holds on tightly to the briefcase, pushes Alice out of the car and gets out of the cab.

Robert Green: Listen, let me be clear. I am not giving those drawings back! They are mine, mine!

Alice: Those drawings belong to Lawrence Windsor and you know it.

Robert Green: Of course not! It was a fair trade-off, a good business opportunity. I just took advantage of it. I didn't even know those drawings were by Turner. You both know that. They could have been anyone's, they could have been worthless. It was my trader's instinct that led me to a good business deal, and now you want to take it away from me!

Natalie: That's ridiculous! You are a liar. You knew that there were valuable items in that house and you convinced an innocent little girl to steal from her own father.

87. THE GUN!

Robert Green is bright red with rage. He is getting more and more angry. He is standing in the middle of Regents Street, facing the two women. Cars are passing by rapidly.

Robert Green: I never told her to steal!

Natalie: You knew perfectly well that the girl was stealing. If not, why would she come to your shop with objects and not money? What's more, you manipulated her to take even more valuable objects each time.

Robert Green: You are crazy. I would never do that! I haven't manipulated anyone. I'm just a businessman. I work with antiques. These are antiques, and they are mine!

Alice: No! They belong to Lawrence Windsor, and you will give them back to their rightful owner!

Robert Green: Is that right? I don't think so!

Natalie: Careful, Alice! He's got a gun!

Alice: Oh my god, Detective Smith was right! He's armed!

Natalie: Mr. Green, put the gun down! Don't do anything stupid.

Robert Green: JUST LEAVE! BECAUSE I'VE HAD ENOUGH OF THIS!

Cab driver: No, I've had enough of this!

88. PETE

The cab driver, seeing that Robert Green gets out a gun and aims it at the two women, takes a small baseball bat from under his seat and slowly approaches Robert Green from behind. When he sees that he is about to shoot, he hits him round the head with all his might. Robert Green falls to the ground, unconscious.

Cab driver: And you better wake up soon, because you own me 7 pounds thirty pence!

Alice: Thank you, Sir! You saved us! I really think he was going to shoot.

Natalie: Do you always carry a baseball bat in your car?

Cab driver: Ha ha ha, no! It's my son's. He has softball practice this afternoon. It was just a coincidence!

Detective Smith: Are you both okay, what happened?

Alice: Robert Green got out of the car and confronted us. He was furious. At one point, he got a gun out! Then this good man came up from behind and knocked him out!

Detective Smith: Thank you very much. What is your name?

Cab driver: I'm Pete. So what's in that briefcase anyway, that has you all so worried?

89. THE BRIEFCASE

Detective Smith handcuffs Robert Green, with his hands behind his back. She radios the police car and tells them to send an ambulance. Then, under the watchful gaze of Natalie, Alice and Pete, she opens the briefcase, which is lying on the ground. Inside are the Turner drawings!

Natalie: I can't believe we finally got them back.

Pete: They're beautiful! Did you do them?

Natalie: No, no, they are by William Turner, one of the greatest painters in the history of British art.

Pete: Turner? Of course, I love his work. I always take my son to the National Gallery; they have several of his paintings there. What are you going to with the drawings now?

Alice: We are going to give them back to their owner, Lawrence Windsor.... And I think you should come with us, since you helped us to get them back.

90. ROBERT GREEN WAKES UP

At that moment, Robert Green wakes up. He seems rather confused at first, but immediately goes back to being furious when he realises he is handcuffed. He tries to get up, but he can't.

Robert Green: What is this? Take these handcuffs off me. I haven't done anything.

Natalie: Is that right?

Robert Green: No, of course not.

Detective Smith: I think you're going to be in handcuffs for a while.

Robert Green: Look, Officer, as I have already explained to these women, I acquired those drawings legally. I have a shop where you can buy and exchange antiques. A customer bought me those drawings and I gave them something very valuable in exchange. It's completely legal!

Detective Smith: Really? Is lying to the police legal? And is aiming a gun at two women legal? If you had told the truth from the beginning, you would be free right now, and most likely with a nice reward from Lawrence Windsor for getting his art back. Instead, you are now going to prison!

Robert Green: Damn!

Pete: Did someone say 'reward'?

91. THE DEPARTURE OF ROBERT GREEN

A short while later, two police cars and an ambulance arrive to take Robert Green away, still in handcuffs to make sure he doesn't try to escape.

Alice: Well, it seems that we won't have to listen to any more of Robert Green's lies....

Natalie: Finally! It's been so exhausting.

Detective Smith: Natalie, Alice, you have really done a great job. If it wasn't for you, we would never have caught him.

Pete: Don't forget about me, Officer!

Detective Smith: Ha ha ha. Of course, Pete. Your role was brief but essential in capturing Robert Green.... You probably saved these women's lives!

Natalie: Your son would be proud.

Pete: I don't think he'll believe anything about what happened today.

Alice: What do we do now?

Detective Smith: It's time to go to Lawrence Windsor's house. We need to get these works of art back home.

92. THE RETURN OF THE DRAWINGS

In police car and Pete's cab, everyone heads to Lawrence Windsor's mansion. They call him on the way. Detective Smith carries the briefcase with the drawings. As they approach the house, Lawrence is waiting for them in the doorway with a huge smile.

Lawrence Windsor: Natalie! Alice! Detective, come in, come in!

Alice: Mr. Windsor! We got them back.

Lawrence Windsor: I know! It's incredible. I am so grateful to you all.

Pete: Hello, I'm Pete. I saved these two at the last minute, just when the thief was about to shoot.

Lawrence Windsor: Really? I can't believe it! Come in, Pete, tell me everything. I want to hear every last detail.

Detective Smith: Natalie, Alice and Pete have done an amazing job. We are very satisfied with their efforts, and now the drawings are back in their rightful home.

Lawrence Windsor: But this isn't their home!

All: What?!

Lawrence Windsor: No, this isn't their home anymore. I've decided to donate my entire collection to the National Gallery!

93. THE DONATION

Everyone looks at Lawrence Windsor, confused. They go through to the living room and ask him for an explanation, after greeting Mariana Windsor, Pauline and the rest of the house staff.

Alice: You are going to donate your entire collection? But you love your collection more than anything else in the world!

Lawrence Windsor: Exactly! I love that collection so much that I think the best thing is for it to be in a place where it will be taken care of as best as possible. At the National Gallery, it won't only be looked after properly, it will have top security. Evidently, this is something that I can no longer guarantee for my collection. Moreover.... I've had a serious talk with Mariana.

Mariana Windsor: That's right. Dad and I have talked and we decided that we both spend too much time thinking about our collections. We should spend more time together, so that's why we have decided to donate them.

Natalie: You're also donating your collection, Mariana?

Mariana Windsor: Yes! I'm just going to keep a few comics to read from time to time, but I'll take the oldest ones to The Cartoon Museum, where they have a huge collection of comics.

Detective Smith: I think that's very selfless of you.

Lawrence Windsor: After everything that's happened, we think it's for the best.

94. THE REWARD

Liz and Jacob bring coffee into the living room for everyone. Then, Natalie and Alice tell Lawrence Windsor everything that has happened since the last time they were at the house. Pete proudly tells his part at the end of the story. Lawrence Windsor waits patiently for them to finish the story and then he makes an announcement.

Lawrence Windsor: Now, I know they will refuse, but I want to say something. I had offered a reward of one thousand pounds to whoever helped me get the artwork back, but I think it's not enough…. Given the value of the works and everything you have done, I think that each person deserves five thousand pounds each! Including Pete, our last-minute hero.

Alice: We couldn't possibly accept that.

Natalie: We don't want any reward, Mr. Windsor.

Pete: I, personally, am happy to accept! I'll finally be able to buy my son a new bike. And maybe one day I will be able to get my own cab.

Alice: You can give our part to Pete, Mr. Windsor. He did save our lives after all! And his son will be so grateful.

Lawrence Windsor: Okay, that seems like a good idea. But at least let me give you something else.

Natalie: It isn't money?

Lawrence Windsor: No, it's not money… it's a surprise. I will give it to you in a week's time, at the National Gallery.

95. THE OPENING

One week later, Alice and Natalie attend the formal opening of the new Windsor Hall at the National Gallery. Lawrence Windsor's collection will be on exhibit to the public in this new space. The two women, who have spent the last week resting in the hotel, are dressed in formal attire, in long ball gowns. Waiters are circulating the room, offering glasses of wine and canapés. The works of art from Lawrence Windsor's collection are on display around the room. On the largest wall, highlighted with special lighting, are the Turner drawings.

Natalie: Pete! You came.

Pete: Yes! Of course. I wouldn't miss this for the world. This is Adam, my son.

Alice: Hi, Adam! Did your father tell you how he saved our lives?

Ali: It's true!? I thought he was making it up.

Natalie: Not at all. Your father is a hero!

Detective Smith: Natalie, Alice! You're here!

Alice: Detective Smith! I almost didn't recognise you with that dress on.

Detective Smith: Ha ha ha. Today is my day off, so you can call me Kelly.

96. THE OFFER

At that moment, Lawrence Windsor enters the room with a woman. He walks straight over to where they are all standing.

Lawrence Windsor: Hello everyone! Detective Smith, how are you? Pete, have you bought your new car yet? I bet it's fast! Ladies!

Alice: Hi, Lawrence! You seem very happy.

Lawrence Windsor: I am, look at my collection! I've never seen my works of art surrounded by so many people, with so much vitality. By the way…. There's someone I'd like you to meet. This is Amelia, the director of the museum.

Amelia: Hi everyone!

Lawrence Windsor: Amelia, I have someone very special to introduce. This is Natalie, the woman I told you about.

Natalie: Hi, Amelia. It's a real honour to meet you. Of course I already know who you are, I've read all your articles about museology.

Amelia: That doesn't surprise me. Lawrence tells me you are very professional and hard-working.

Natalie: Well, I'm not sure about that.

Amelia: Well I know for a fact that you are, your university told me you graduated with honours, top of your class!

Natalie: You called my university?

Amelia: Absolutely! I wouldn't hire a new curator for the museum without checking their academic records first. And I have to say, yours are impeccable!

Natalie: Me, your new curator?! Here at the National Gallery?!

Amelia: Of course, who better to take care of our new exhibition hall?

97. THE SECOND OFFER

Natalie tears up with emotion. It's her dream job! Alice hugs her with joy.

Alice: Natalie, I'm so happy for you. That means we can live in London! We can look for an apartment in Camden, now that we know the area so well.

Lawrence Windsor: Do you know what you want to do here, Alice?

Alice: Yes, the same as always: write! I want to write a story about the robbery, I think it would be an excellent true crime story.

Lawrence Windsor: I'm so glad to hear you say that, because it's exactly what I have in mind.

Alice: What do you mean?

Lawrence Windsor: A few days ago, I called my good friend Thomas Richter, from the publication Raymond.

Alice: Raymond?! That's my favourite police crime publication.

Lawrence Windsor: Yes, they're the best. Thomas is a very good friend of mine. Finally, I told him about the robbery and he also thinks it will make perfect material for a novel. But we are a bit concerned....

Alice: Why's that?

Lawrence Windsor: Well, because we don't have anyone to write it…. If only we knew a writer specialising in police crime novels that knew every detail of the robbery…. Wait a minute! What about you?

Alice: Are you serious? You want me to write a novel for the Raymond publication? That's my dream!

Lawrence Windsor: Great, because they already have the contract ready for you to sign. Thomas will see you at 10am tomorrow in his office.

Natalie: ALICE, ALICE! Are you okay? She's fainted!

98. LAWRENCE WINDSOR'S SPEECH

Alice recovers quickly, and she can't believe what Lawrence has done for her. Both women feel like they are in a dream. Just then, Lawrence Windsor clinks his glass to get everyone's attention.

Lawrence Windsor: Friends, colleagues. I'd like to propose a toast. Firstly, I'd like to propose a toast to art. These works you see around you have brought me a lot of happiness over the years. Now, I sincerely hope that they bring happiness to everyone who comes to see them here at the National Gallery. I would like to thank Amelia for accepting my donation, and for opening the museum's doors to provide such a wonderful space for the collection. But, most of all, I'd like to thank four people without whom these three original Turner drawings wouldn't be here: Detective Smith, Pete, Alice and Natalie. A toast to them! Cheers!

99. THE MAP

Everyone toasts and claps. Natalie and Alice look at each other and raise their glasses to a new life in London. They are very excited by everything that is to yet to come. Then, a waiter comes over with a note.

Waiter: Are you Alice and Natalie? I have a message for you both.

Natalie: What is that? What does it say?

Alice: It says "Follow the map to the point marked X". There's a floor plan of the museum with a trail marked from where we are right now to a small room marked X.

Natalie: What do you say? Are you ready to follow clues again? To solve a new mystery?

Alice: I don't think it's a mystery, I think I know exactly what it's about….

Natalie: Well, let's go then.

Pete: Hey! Where are you going?

Alice: We'll be back soon.

Pete: Don't get into any trouble. I might not be there to save you.

Alice: Got it!

100. A SPECIAL INVITATION

The two women follow the map of the museum as specified in the note: they go up the first set of stairs, turn right and go in the first door on the left, then up a narrow stairway into a small room.

Natalie: It's the man in the hat!

Adam: You can call me Bernard, that's my name!

Alice: Hi, Bernard. I wondered when we'd see you again.

Adam: It wasn't my intention to take you away from the party, but I wanted to congratulate you on solving the mystery, and on your new jobs!

Natalie: How do you know about that?

Adam: At the Historians' Club we know a lot of things.... Speaking of which, it is my honour to give you these.

Alice: What are they?

Adam: Open the envelopes. Inside you will find two invitations to be members of the Historians' Club.

Natalie: Adam, it would be an honour....

Alice: Does that mean we can help you to solve mysteries?

Adam: Exactly! We will let you know whenever we might need your help. Are you interested?

Alice and Natalie: Of course!

Adam: I'm so pleased. Now go back to the party! Your friends are waiting for you. And remember, don't tell anyone about this! It's a secret.

101. THE WINDSORS

When they go back to the opening party, Detective Smith runs towards them.

Detective Smith: Where were you both? We just got an important call a few minutes ago!

Alice: What happened? Is everything okay?

Detective Smith: Yes, everything's fine. It's just that... the Windsors want to thank you personally for recovering the Turner works.

Natalie: What do you mean, Lawrence and Mariana already thanked us in person several times.

Detective Smith: No, not those Windsors! The Windsors. The royal family! They are waiting for you at the palace....

THE END

THANKS FOR READING!

I hope you have enjoyed this book and that your language skills have improved as a result!

A lot of hard work went into creating this book, and if you would like to support me, the best way to do so would be to leave an honest review of the book on the store where you made your purchase.

Want to get in touch? I love hearing from readers. Reach out to me any time at *olly@storylearning.com*

To your success,

Olly Richards

MORE FROM OLLY

If you have enjoyed this book, you will love all the other free language learning content I publish each week on my blog and podcast: *StoryLearning*.

Blog: Study hacks and mind tools for independent language learners.

www.storylearning.com

Podcast: I answer your language learning questions twice a week on the podcast.

www.storylearning.com/itunes

YouTube: Videos, case studies, and language learning experiments.

https://www.youtube.com/ollyrichards

COURSES FROM OLLY RICHARDS

If you've enjoyed this book, you may be interested in Olly Richards' complete range of language courses, which employ his StoryLearning® method to help you reach fluency in your target language.

Critically acclaimed and popular among students, Olly's courses are available in multiple languages and for learners at different levels, from complete beginner to intermediate and advanced.

To find out more about these courses, follow the link below and select "Courses" from the menu bar:

https://storylearning.com/courses

"Olly's language-learning insights are right in line with the best of what we know from neuroscience and cognitive psychology about how to learn effectively. I love his work!"

Dr. Barbara Oakley,
Bestselling Author of "A Mind for Numbers"

Lightning Source UK Ltd.
Milton Keynes UK
UKHW012329270122
397812UK00002B/173